CW00822466

To all our wonderful Body Retreaters without whose feedback and encouragement this book would not have been written and to my "team" J, K, & W for everything x

MORE CONSCIOUS COOKING

Food Philosophy and recipes from The Body Retreat kitchen

Cook Well Live Well Eat Well

Juls Abernethy

Photography by Yolande de Vries

CONTENTS

PREFACE

As a health writer and retreat reviewer I have visited a ridiculous number of retreats all over the world. I've undergone intense ayurvedic panchakarma, chewed stale spelt rolls on the Mayr cure, sipped just juice for ten days, gnawed my way through piles of raw food and subsisted on cabbage gruel and the occasional raisin (I nearly passed out on the last one).

Yet the one retreat I return to time and time again for my personal wellbeing is The Body Retreat. Truly, I have forgotten how many times I've visited but, every time I do, I feel the tension drop off my shoulders the moment I walk through the door – it's like coming home. I love it because Juls and Julie have huge integrity, years of expertise and acres of knowledge, plus they are just the kindest, loveliest women. They don't offer gimmicks; they don't bedazzle with fancy equipment or arcane regimes. In fact, everything is so simple and straightforward you wonder if it can possibly work. Yet it does, it really does. If anyone tells me they want to lose weight and gain a healthy relationship with their body, I always point them towards The Body Retreat. You are not only guaranteed to lose weight and get a lot fitter very swiftly but (and here's the part I really love) your stay is just the kick-starter – when you get home, you'll be armed with a toolkit of simple effective fitness regimes and amazing meal plans. For sure many retreats send you home with swathes of information, but usually the plans are too complex, the menus too fiddly. Even though you may have the very best intentions, you swiftly fall by the wayside. Hand on heart, this is the one retreat that sticks with me – because it just slots so easily into my frenetic everyday life.

Food is celebrated here, not villainised. Every meal is calibrated to give you exactly the nutrients and energy you need – yet this is never dismal 'diet' food. In fact, The Body Retreat is vehemently 'anti-diet'. Instead, you learn how to change your relationship with food for good. Juls carefully picks meals that even the most lackluster home cook (like me) can create easily at home. You learn how to eat mindfully; how to figure out why you're making food choices; how to become conscious around food.

I would also add that Body Retreat meals are always delicious. They don't only tickle taste buds but leave you feeling fully satisfied. Many of the recipes have become my kitchen staples, from Breakfast Burritos, Beetroot Burgers, the Goats' Cheese Salad and last but not least Chia Seed Porridge (although I've not forgiven Juls for her Shrek Break version...luckily this didn't make it into the book!!)

So I'm over-the-moon that all my favourite recipes and more are now available in this cookbook. Everything is simple to prepare and cook, and the majority of recipes freeze well too, which is a huge boon.

This is real food for real women; women like me who love eating but want to get and stay healthy without feeling deprived. I wish you happy cooking and happy eating!

Jane Alexander
Writer, Journalist, Holistic Wellness Guru

INTRODUCTION

Firstly, let me tell you what you don't have in your hands... This is Not a diet book.

Between these pages you won't find a list prescribing what you "should" be eating. There are no strict rules to be followed.

This is not a short-term eating programme.

This is a book to encourage you to enjoy a positive relationship with food so that you feel energised, strong and healthy.

To feel confident to begin eating in a way that nourishes body and brain.

Back in 2016 we produced our first cookery book, Conscious Cooking, in response to the demand from our retreat community for more recipes. It would be putting it mildly to say that I didn't enjoy the process.

So, it took me a while to feel able to begin the process all over again. Which is why the working title for this book is Conscious Cooking – The Revenge.

In your hands you hold The Body Retreat food philosophy alongside a collection of recipes that we enjoy on retreat.

Food is dynamic, it is always changing, the cucumber you bought two days ago is different today – it contains more water. The banana sitting in the fruit bowl for 48 hours has more sugar; the piece of meat in the fridge will be a little dryer even overnight.

For this reason, it is so important to keep tasting and watching your food as you cook. This allows you to make little tweaks as you go along. I'm a very instinctive cook but I appreciate that not everyone is. I meet so many women on retreat who are nervous about cooking, who have never really cooked, and they like to follow a recipe To the Letter.

That's a great place to start. Follow the recipes in the book and then use this first dish as your guide for future. Then every time you make it again, you'll feel a little more confident and you can start to add your personal touches and make to your specific tastes.

ALL ABOUT

ABOUT THE BODY RETREAT

The Body Retreat is a destination for women who are ready to reclaim their body, health and wellbeing that they deserve. Our Women Only Health Retreats bridge the gap between boot camp and spa holiday.

Our Retreats cover all health aspects for women: diet, nutrition, stress, sleep, exercise, fitness, rehabilitation, hormonal balance, emotional strength and improved personal confidence. Our mission is to offer a solution for every woman, but an individual one, not one size fits all.

For some women that's turning their backs on decades of dodgy dieting and finally achieving the body and fitness they want; for others it's about regaining energy and zest for life.

Some women join The Body Retreat because they realise that something has to change with their current lifestyle, but they are not sure what to do or how to begin, and many women join simply because they enjoy having the space and time to focus on themselves for a change.

At The Body Retreat we understand from both personal experience and from our years of study, training and expertise that when it comes to losing weight, getting fit, managing stress or any other wellbeing goal, women need to attend to both their mental and emotional health at the same time as their physical bodies. So The Body Retreat does just that. Clears confusion around health and diets, debunks myths and puts women back in control of their health.

ABOUT JULS

I have always loved my food. I enjoyed the art of creating dishes and menus, I love getting creative in the kitchen. I enjoy the actual process of cooking when you start to see, and more importantly taste, the dish coming together; and I love the final part of the process where you sit down and enjoy the fruits of your labours.

When we first started The Body Retreat, we had a cook at the venue we used. Unfortunately, they were not used to the style of cooking that we needed on retreat and so they were very inconsistent. I was taught very early in my hospitality career that Quality is Consistency and so it really grated on me that we could not be consistent.

Eventually we parted ways and I suggested to Julie that I step into the kitchen until we found a new cook. My first degree was in Hotel & Catering Management, during which I had learnt the basics of cooking, and to refresh my skills I went to Ashburton Cookery School in Devon.

I loved being in the kitchen. It was and still is a lot of fun. Now I am very fortunate to be supported in The Body Retreat Kitchen, which allows me to take a slight step back and focus on other aspects of Retreat...but I'm always happy to pop my apron on and get cooking.

My cooking has changed a lot since our first Conscious Cooking book...mostly as a result of my own health challenges.

In the last few years I was diagnosed with GORD and SIBO. I was also battling a number of seemingly unrelated conditions: anxiety, fatigue, gas and bloating, insomnia, daily full body rashes, a staphylococcus infection on my face. I was helping to run a health retreat and I was falling apart. Finally, I took the decision to privately have a full set of tests undertaken. I tested blood, breath, spit, wee, poo ... the whole gambit. The diagnosis was that I had Hashimoto's disease and a Leaky Gut.

I have never been one to pop a pill or apply a potion as my first action. I have long believed that the fork is mightier that the prescription and so for all my conditions I have turned to nutrition and lifestyle changes as my first course of action.

Today as I write this introduction, I am symptom free and still medication free and I have learnt so much about food, nutrition and eating for healing. I've been able to share my knowledge along the way on our retreats and I do pride myself that there is no dietary requirement that we cannot support on retreat. Throughout the book we will be sharing tips on how you can make certain recipes work better for your own health goals.

WHAT IS CONSCIOUS COOKING

Conscious Cooking is about making a conscious choice at every stage of the food journey.

We always have a choice, but so often we find ourselves sleep walking through our choices, these unconscious choices soon become habit and then it feels all but impossible to change. You feel stuck.

Conscious Cooking is about going right back to the beginning... Thinking about food in a new way. Choosing food that nourishes, balances and makes you happy. You consciously choose to tick all three boxes.

For example, you have had a hard day at work and you arrive through the door at home feeling ravenous. You still have your coat on, and you are rummaging through the fridge and cupboards looking for the perfect thing to eat. You want it to be quick and filling. You might choose toast, cereal or crackers as they will give you an immediate feeling of happiness.

However, on their own they won't nourish your body and brain, and they definitely won't leave you feeling balanced...if anything quite the opposite...you're most likely to find yourself back in the kitchen in an hour looking for something else.

Or maybe you are being good, and you make yourself a "healthy" vegetable soup for lunch – you eat it feeling very virtuous, even though you don't really enjoy it. You know it's a well-balanced meal, you know it's good for your body, but boy is it boring. So, guess what... in about an hour you find yourself pacing the kitchen looking for something nice to have.

These are just a couple of examples of patterns that you might be stuck in unconsciously... you may not be conscious of the habit, but you are very aware, sometimes painfully aware, of the outcome of these habits.

Conscious Cooking as I say is about going back to basics, it's about creating a virtuous cycle of eating in a way that nourishes you, balances you and makes you happy.

WHAT IS THE BODY RETREAT FOOD PHILOSOPHY?

The Body Retreat is Anti Diet... diets are restrictive eating plans often with a finite date. You start to change your food with the intention of losing weight... and then as soon as you reach your goal... perhaps it's a date that you are working towards for a special event or holiday or to get into your dress, your bikini or skinny jeans. Then you stop ... you go back to your old ways and soon the unwanted weight starts to creep back on.

This is a book to help change your relationship with food for good.

Many books that aim to help you change your body and your health are about restriction, deprivation...they can almost feel anti-food, viewing food as only fuel.

Rightly or wrongly, food is much more than that. Food can be joy, comfort, it can be a staple part of life, a way to show yourself and others that you care. Now of course, our relationships with food can be shaped by life experiences, especially our childhood. If you have experienced loss, abuse, trauma, deprivation, scarcity, punishment...to name but a few experiences...if you have experienced these in childhood they can create an unhealthy relationship with food that lasts for decades.

This can be why when you have been challenged on something at work your default is to go and gorge yourself on chocolate, or why when you feel under the weather you feel the need to carb load.

This is why at The Body Retreat when it comes to eating, we ask four questions.

- What are you eating?
- When are you eating it?
- How are you eating it?

And finally and very importantly

- Why are you eating it?

This is The Body Retreat's Food Philosophy.

It's about so much more than just fuel, or calorie deficit. It is about nourishment, balance and happiness. When you eat in a way that ticks those three boxes you are a winner.

These recipes are a selection of the way we eat on retreat. The meals are based on good quality protein for repair, maintenance and growth; essential fats for healthy heart, cell health and metabolic function; dietary fibre to support good gut health and help you feel satisfied; low glycaemic carbohydrates to prevent blood sugar highs and lows; and a whole lot of fruit, salad and vegetables to ensure sufficient vitamin and mineral intake.

Conscious Cooking is more than just a collection of retreat food recipes ...our retreat food is designed to be real food for real women who want to achieve and maintain real results.

There is no magic in these pages. If anything it really is pretty much back to basics. You take a balance of simple ingredients, prepared simply and with minimum fuss. Choosing to eat in a way that nourishes your body and your brain so that you feel energised, vibrant, strong and healthy...as a by-product you will find that you will also start to shed the weight that is unnecessary for you.

But this is a book that goes beyond just what to eat...because at The Body Retreat we believe that before you eat you need to ask yourself the questions WHAT, WHEN, HOW and WHY.

What you eat – ensuring that you are eating the right balance of foods so that you get the energy and nutrition that you need.

When you eat – thinking about eating in a way that balances your energy levels so that you do not fall foul of low blood sugar or carb cravings.

How you eat – you are not simply what you eat...rather you are what you absorb. So, eating in a manner that actively promotes gut health, balanced energy and optimum notional absorption is critical.

Why are you eating – how many times have you found yourself eating when you were not truly physically hungry? Whether from habit, environmental cues, emotional triggers or a deeply rooted psychological hunger, it might be time to really get clear on why you are choosing to eat.

The book combines the health and wellness philosophy of The Body Retreat.

THE WHAT, WHEN, HOW & WHY YOU EAT

Food is much more than just calories. It is much more than just fuel.

For too long we have been fed the line that we should eat less and move more if we want to lose weight. Creating energy deficit is all important. This thinking means that people start to view food as just a collection of calories. This leads to a disordered relationship with food, it leads people to underfeed themselves, to under-nourish their body and brain. It can also lead to cravings, binges, weight gain and ill health.

WHAT

For too long women have been told to fill up on low calorie foods... very often this means that they end up consuming a lot of simple sugars (for example – cakes, sweets, fruit juice, some fruit yogurts or condiments), refined carbs (for example – white flour bread, pasta, rice, pastries, breakfast cereals) and processed foods (for example – ready meals, pizzas, burgers, white bread, savoury snacks, crisps, pies, pastries, biscuits, processed meat, eg bacon, sausages, pate) while avoiding high fat/ high calorie foods. The trouble is that these processed foods and simple carbs do not keep you satisfied or balanced.

I don't want this book to get all sciencey... but it is important to understand how our bodies respond to different types of food. Processed foods, refined carbs and simple sugars are broken down into glucose relatively quickly and therefore have a more pronounced effect on blood sugar levels than either fat or protein. Your blood sugar goes up fast! You feel amazing, full of energy. But what goes up fast comes down fast! You get a crash, a slump, feel a craving for more glucose. Very quickly this becomes a vicious cycle. You find yourself eating to feel "normal".

When you change the focus on all your main meals to contain Protein, Fat and Fibre you find that you have a much slower energy release... and what goes up slow...comes down slow. Bye bye crashes, slumps and craving!! Yes REALLY.

Proteins

We need protein in our meals as it helps to slow the release of sugar. But what is protein and why do we need it? Protein is a macro-nutrient and is made up of amino acids. Some amino acids are essential as we can only get them from our diet. We need amino acids as they are the body's building blocks both in cells' structure and function, for example in muscles, bones and skin all need adequate protein for both structure and function. Good protein sources are meat, fish, dairy, eggs, nuts, seeds, beans and lentils.

Fats

We need fats in our diet as an energy source, for skin, hair and to absorb important fat-soluble vitamins and hormones. There are different types of fats; we need essential fatty acids from food for our brains and they are anti-inflammatory; good sources are oily fish, nuts, seeds, avocados. We want more of the unsaturated fats which can be found in rapeseed oil, for example. Rapeseed oil is recommended for cooking as it has a high heat point, meaning it is less likely to get damaged and form harmful compounds compared to other oils. In your diet you also want to include limited amounts of saturated fats, found in animal products such as meat, dairy and coconut oil, while avoiding trans fats as much as possible which are found in processed foods and can damage our cells.

Fibre

Fibre is found in plant-based carbohydrates, fibre is not digested in the small intestine but travels through to the large intestine; it is food to help feed the good bacteria in the gut and keeps the gut functioning optimally. It has also been shown to help with heart health and for type 2 diabetes. Fibre also helps to slow the release of sugars; imagine eating an apple to having a glass of apple juice – the spike in blood sugar is much higher from the juice, but eating an apple with the fibre slows the release and is better for blood sugar stabilisation. Good sources of fibre are fruit and vegetables, whole grains, nuts and oats and starchy vegetables – like potatoes and especially if you keep the skin on.

You'll find that all our recipes provide this balance.

WHEN

As the saying goes, timing is everything. Having said that, there is NO one size fits all on when you should eat your meals. I know that it would be much simpler for me to tell you to eat at 8.00am/1.00pm/6.00pm...but that doesn't work.

Firstly, we all have different bodies and so different rhythms. We also have different schedules and demands on our time. Some of us are larks and some night owls.

What we can do is apply the same principles to When we eat.

We recommend that you eat three main meals and one snack per day. This is normally set out as Breakfast, Lunch, Afternoon Snack and Supper. The actual time of these meals is not important. What is important is the timing between the meals.

Let's start with breakfast. Often championed as 'the most important meal of the day' ... nonsense. Breakfast is no more important a meal than the others... what is important is How You Break Your Fast. This brings us back to WHAT to eat. Break your fast with cereal, low fat milk, toast and coffee and you'll be craving a pick me up by 10.30 am. Choose to break your fast with a meal rich in protein, fat and fibre and you will give yourself sustained energy for up to five hours!!! How amazing is that.

So, let's say you break your fast at 7.00am then you'll be looking to lunch about 12 midday. Your energy should sustain you through to then. Breakfast at 9am then you're good until about 2pm...you can see where I'm going with this. Of course, this is all contingent on WHAT you eat.

HOW

You have probably heard it said that you are what you eat. We don't buy that... you are not just what you eat... you are what you absorb, and this is much more about How you eat.

Let me explain.

It's time we got back to listening to our bodies and forming a better relationship with food. Your body knows how to eat in a way that allows it to digest and absorb all the nutrients and energy from food. But our digestive system isn't on the same wavelength as modern life.

Digestion is a slow old process and rightly so. You may well be able to gulp down a meal standing up in under five minutes ...but your body does not work as quickly as that. The digestive process is designed specifically to be slow, to allow the food to be broken down so it can be absorbed.

Every step of the digestion process is essential to allow your body to take what it needs from the food. From the enzymes in your saliva, the slow peristalsis movement of your oesophagus, the wonderful bowl of digestive enzymes that is the gut, the little villi in the intestine whose job it is to not only make that energy and nutrition exchange but also to move along what is not used to be excreted as waste. All of this process is sllllooooooowwwwww. You cannot rush biology.

It's time to slow everything down.

General Guidelines

1. Eat whenever you are hungry. (Truly hungry, body hungry not mind hungry.)
2. Eat sitting down in a calm environment. This does not include the car while you are driving.
3. Eat without distractions. Distractions include television, newspaper, books, intense or anxiety producing conversation. Be careful of loud pumping music – you will begin to eat to the beat.
4. Eat only what your body wants and needs. (Big difference from what your MIND wants!)
5. Eat until you are satisfied. (This is different to full.) Remind yourself: If I continue eating when I am no longer hungry it is the same thing as throwing it away. It is better to throw it in the rubbish or compost heap rather than make your belly the bin!!
6. Eat (with the intention of being) in full view of others. No Secret eating.
7. Eat with enjoyment and pleasure.

WHY

Last but by no means least... think about why you are eating. Are you eating when you are truly physically hungry? Or perhaps you have fallen into the habit of eating when you experience external cues or emotional triggers?

When you start to listen to your body and learn how to respond to the true cues of physical hunger, when you choose to nourish your body and brain with good quality proteins, fibre and fats which not only satisfy you but also keep you fuller for longer, you will find that you are no longer a slave to cravings. Once your physical hunger is satisfied then you can focus on the question of why you want to eat at other times.

WHAT, WHEN, HOW & WHY... I'm sure by now you have figured out that these questions and therefore their answers are all interconnected.

Focus on just one question and you will find yourself falling back into old habits and behaviours once more.

Conscious Cooking
@ The Body Retreat

24 HOURS ON YOUR PLATE

BREAKFAST

Breakfast isn't the most important meal of the day but how you break your fast is probably the most important nutritional decision you will make as it will either set you up for a successful balanced day or could set you off on the blood sugar roller coaster. I really love breakfast; it probably is my most favourite meal. Who says that you can only eat breakfast meals at the start of the day – why not enjoy pancakes, or eggs or oats for lunch or supper? Make the meals work for you and your lifestyle.

LIGHT BITES vs MAIN MEALS

When do you have your main meal? For many the main meal of the day is taken in the evening when there is more time to both prepare and enjoy the meal. But you can find that eating a large meal in the evening can leave you feeling sluggish the next morning... there may not have been enough time after the meal to allow for full digestion and so while you try to sleep your body is still trying to digest...which means that you do both things poorly.

SNACKS

On retreat we advocate that you enjoy three main meals and one afternoon snack every day. No eating between meals...there really should be no need. If you have fueled yourself well at your meal, then you know that you have given yourself 3-5 hours of energy. So, wanting to eat between meals is either habitual or psychological. Don't fall into this trap. Having one small protein-based snack each afternoon allows you to finish work, survive your commute and then still have the energy and desire to make yourself a healthy, nutritious meal when you arrive home.

SWEET TREATS

Life is too short to not have a little sweetness in it. The sweet treats in this book can be enjoyed in moderation as part of your 80%...but portion size is key. If you start to have a double or triple portion every day then you will find that you soon feel out of balance, your appetite will grow as well as your waistline. Save your indulgence for your 20%.

TIME TO GET CONSCIOUS

CONSCIOUS PLANNING

Planning is the key to enjoying balance. I know that to begin with it can feel like you have "another job" to do. But you know the universal truth is failing to plan is planning to fail.

Making time at the weekend to look at your week ahead, noting days that are super busy, days where you will be traveling, days when you are socialising. Once you can see at a glance what is coming in the next week then it's time to make a plan...stop crossing your fingers and hoping for the best, hoping that you will remember to make a good choice, hoping that there will be a healthy choice available, hoping that you are not too tired to cook... That's a lot of hope.

Instead... get planning. A simple sheet of A4 paper. Three main meals and one snack per day. What will they be? How will they be prepared or cooked? How do you create balance in your week? How do you enjoy some indulgence? Get it planned in...then relax.

CONSCIOUS SHOPPING

Make the majority of what you eat Real Produce, because the closer you are to nature the closer you are to health...so the majority of the items in your basket won't have a barcode on them.

But of course we all live in the real world and there are times when it really isn't the best choice to start from scratch; sometimes you really don't have the time or the skill, or maybe it's because there is a really great product that is not packed with additives, artificial sweeteners, added sugars or a raft of unpronounceable ingredients.

But get label savvy.

Product ingredients are listed by quantity – from highest to lowest amount. This means that the first ingredient is what the manufacturer used the most of. A good rule of thumb is to scan the first three ingredients, as they make up the largest part of what you're eating. If you are surprised by what you see or don't know what the ingredient is...put it back on the shelf.

Stay away from the traffic light system. The traffic light system marks fats, saturated fats, sugar and salt, as red for high, amber for medium and green for low amounts of these nutrients. It was designed to help us make better choices, but it can be very misleading, as it is too simplistic. It doesn't take into account portion sizes, as having three greens doesn't always cancel out a red, and different combinations of colours doesn't always mean you are making a healthier choice and can be confusing. You can still get highly processed foods that may have three greens, for example.

CONSCIOUS EATING

This is the practice we follow on ALL our Retreats. This allows you to set up your body to digest and absorb the nutrients and energy from the food you have eaten.

1. Posture. Three deep breaths in and on every out breath roll your shoulder blades down your back. Release any physical tension and sit up straight to aid digestion.
2. Hunger Scale (1–10). How hungry does your body feel? Really listen.
3. Be mindful of the food on your plate, appreciate the colours and textures on your plate.
4. Smell your first fork/spoonful. Engage your olfactory senses to waken your digestive system.
5. Put your cutlery down between each and every mouthful.
6. Chew slowly so you can savour taste, temperature and textures, and clear your mouth before you pick up your cutlery for the next mouthful.
7. Stop eating when you feel satisfied, not full up.
8. Always leave something on your plate. You control your plate; your plate does not control you!
9. No Water... do not dilute your digestive enzymes.

CONSCIOUS COOKING

Conscious Cooking is about thinking about the look, taste, texture, temperature and even the sound of the dish. You want to sit down to a dish of food that excites the senses, that makes your mouth water when you look at it or smell it. That while you are eating is keeping you interested mouthful after mouthful as the tastes and textures change as you eat.

SET UP A
CONSCIOUS
KITCHEN

THE CONSCIOUS LARDER

A well-stocked store cupboard is the first step towards being able to cook tasty and healthy meals. Here is a list of the items that I try to keep stocked up in The Body Retreat kitchen cupboard all of the time:

Oils

- Coconut Oil
- Cold pressed extra virgin Rapeseed Oil
- Cocoa butter

Vinegars/Sauces

- Raw Unfiltered Apple Cider Vinegar
- Balsamic Vinegar
- Red wine Vinegar
- Organic Tamari Sauce or Soy sauce
- Wholegrain Mustard
- Dijon Mustard
- Ground Mustard
- Tamarind Paste
- Chilli Sauce
- Red curry paste
- Harissa paste
- Sugar-free Apple sauce
- Fish sauce

Herbs/Spices

- Sea Salt
- Black pepper
- Dried Basil
- Dried Oregano
- Dried Bay Leaves
- Dried Thyme
- Dried Rosemary
- Ground Cumin
- Ground Coriander
- Ground Ginger
- Ground Cinnamon
- Sweet Smoked Paprika
- Turmeric
- Mild Chilli Powder
- Dried Chilli Flakes
- Mild Curry Powder
- Garam Masala
- Nutritional Yeast
- Cardamom pods
- Ground Nutmeg
- Mixed all spice
- Cumin seeds
- Fennel seeds
- Bouillon Vegetable stock
- Lemongrass

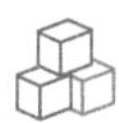

Sugars

- Local raw unpasteurised Honey
- Organic Maple Syrup
- Coconut Sugar
- Vanilla pods
- Vanilla Extract

Dried Fruit

- Medjool Dates
- Raisins/Sultanas
- Dried Coconut flakes
- Desiccated coconut
- Dried Cranberry
- Dried Figs
- Dried Apricots

Nuts/Seeds

- Pecans
- Unblanched Almonds
- Almond Flakes
- Walnuts
- Meridian 100% Peanut Butter
- Meridian 100% Almond Butter
- Meridian Cashew nut butter
- Ground Flaxseed
- Brazil Nuts
- Pumpkin Seeds
- Sunflower Seeds
- Chia Seeds
- Cashew nuts
- Ground almonds
- Linseeds
- Hulled hemp seed
- Pine nuts
- Pistachios
- Psyllium husks

Tins/Cartons

- Chopped Tomatoes
- Passata
- Tomato Puree
- Cannellini Beans
- Butter Beans
- Haricot Beans
- Kidney Beans
- Black Beans
- Black eye Beans
- Borlotti Beans
- Chickpeas
- Tinned Lentils
- White beans
- Coconut milk
- Jar sundried tomatoes
- Jar of anchovies
- Coconut cream
- Coconut milk

Dried Items

- Tri colour Quinoa
- Quinoa Flakes
- Raw Buckwheat Groats
- Buckwheat Flour
- Rice flour
- Oat flour
- Almond flour
- Wholegrain flour
- Quick action yeast
- Red Lentils
- Green lentils
- Yellow lentils
- Wholegrain basmati rice
- Jumbo Rolled Porridge Oats
- Raw Cacao Powder
- Cacao nibs
- Baking powder
- Bicarbonate of soda
- Dried mixed mushrooms
- Greens powder
- Nut milks
- Coconut water
- Vegan yeast
- Wild rice

Freezer

- Rye bread
- Frozen cranberries
- Frozen sweetcorn
- Frozen peas
- Frozen petite pois
- Fish and meat

CONSCIOUS KITCHEN EQUIPMENT

Making healthy tasty dishes is certainly a lot easier and a lot nicer when you have some equipment to hand. You will find that you spend much less time in the kitchen and the time you do spend you enjoy more.

A decent Chef's Knife.

Cooks and chefs love their knives; we get very protective about them. I even have rules about how my knives can be washed on retreat LOL. It is true that using the right knife for the right job does make things so much easier; it is much harder to bone a chicken, fillet a fish, chop an onion and segment an orange all with the same knife. But it is also very true that you need to only start with ONE good knife. The most important knife is the all-purpose, versatile, sturdy, roughly eight-inch chef's knife.

NutriBullet

I use my NutriBullet every single day and the very first time I made a smoothie in this, it was the smoothest I've ever gotten my breakfast smoothie to be. It's also incredibly useful for making homemade flours and I routinely make homemade oat flour in it. It's great for blender recipes too, especially if you want to make smaller portions.

Food Processor

A food processor is incredibly versatile since you could use it for something as simple as cutting up veggies for a larger meal, making your own nut butter, making hummus and spreads, chopping nuts, making amazing dairy-free ice creams.

Hand Mixer

For me I like a hand mixer to whisk eggs, whip cream and even mix cake batter every now and then; a hand mixer is a better option than a full-sized stand mixer as you can easily store it in a drawer when not using.

Baking trays

I feel that you need about half a dozen baking trays, of varying depths and size. You can use for roasting veggies, warming up spiralised spaghetti, making flapjacks, granolas, cookies. You can also use small baking trays to freeze fruits separated out so they don't stick together before then decanting into a box or bag for storage in the freezer.

Measuring spoons

When you are getting started in the kitchen these are your go-to for specific measuring to ensure that the food you're making is still healthy. I promise, it's very easy to accidentally add 3 tablespoons of sugar/coconut oil when you think you're pouring only 1 tablespoon!

Spatulas

This is probably my all-time favourite kitchen kit list item. I have about 4 in every kitchen tool box. Great for scraping smoothies and hummus out of the blender or food processor so no waste. Perfect for making sauces when you need to blend together. I even use them to make scrambled eggs. Like the baking trays, get a couple in various sizes.

Colander

From washing veggies, draining pasta, dccanting stocks and broths, this unassuming bit of kitchen equipment is just so essential that spend just a week without it and you'll soon discover just how often you reach for it.

Sieves

I had to separate these from a colander since they have two completely different purposes. I use my sieves (both large and mini) to remove seeds from limes and lemons, to drain the liquid from canned beans and then rinse them. They are very convenient and the fine mesh means that no matter how small the food, it won't fall through, which is why you can't use a colander in place of a strainer. I also use my strainer to pre-wash my quinoa or lentils all the time.

Spiraliser

Now I will admit that this piece of equipment is a one trick pony...but boy what a trick. A spiralizer is probably one of the coolest kitchen tools ever invented. Do you love pasta? I do. Making curly pasta noodles out of veggies... delicious and nutritious.

BEYOND CONSCIOUS COOKING

As I said in the beginning this is Not a Diet Book. This is not a faddy way of eating until you shed a few pounds and inches. This is a way of eating for life.

The philosophy of eating consciously means that you begin to find real enjoyment in food again, but you look at food differently. You look for food that nourishes your mind and your body. You look for food that is close to nature. You look for food that is interesting to your senses. You begin to make more conscious choices about what goes on your plate.

One question I am asked on almost every retreat is "how much" should I be eating at each meal, of any particular ingredient etc, etc.

It is an almost impossible question to answer... what you eat in any particular sitting depends on who you are, how well you have slept, how hydrated you are, how active you have been or plan to be, what you have eaten in previous meals.

So what I do share with our retreaters is the Use Your Hands Principle.

Did you know that you own stomach is roughly the same size as your own clenched fist? Keep that in mind as you are planning your meals.

When it comes to How Much to eat, the first thing is to start with is your plate size. Most modern dinner service plates are between 14-16 inches big...that is HUGE!! Your portion can be measured by holding your hands together, thumbs tucked in...what is under your hands is YOUR portion. Now some of you may be shocked by how small that looks, but when you change up the composition of the food that goes on your plate you will start to feel very satisfied portion after portion.

Measure your Plate

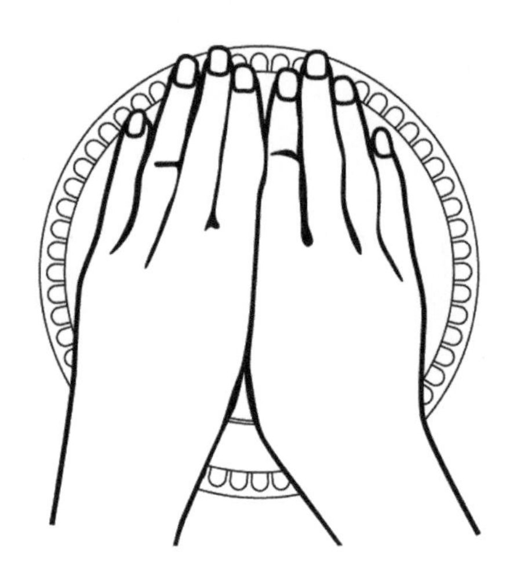

Ok, next... what goes on the plate.

Vegetables and Salad

A heaped Handful.

Fruit

What you can comfortably hold in the palm of your hand

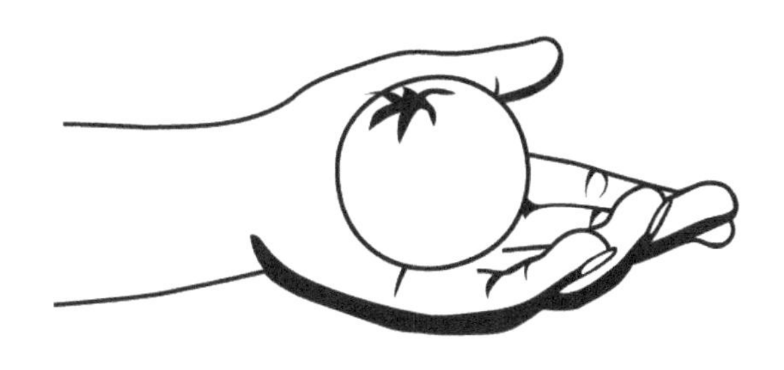

Starches, Grains, Cereals

A palmful.

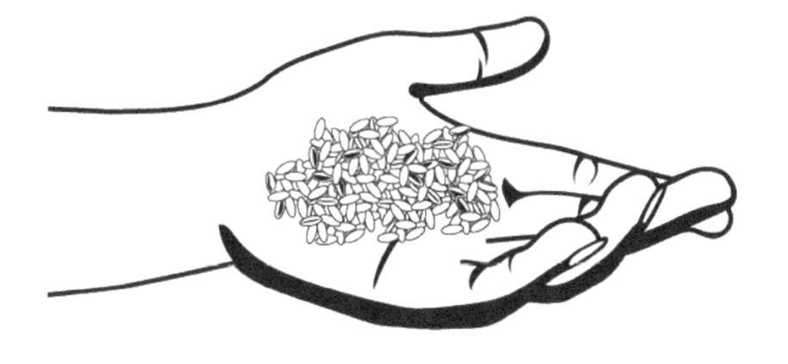

Fats

The size of your thumb.

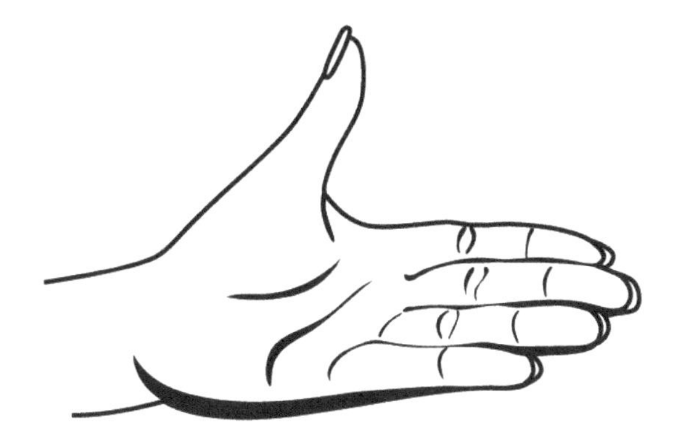

Proteins

The flat of the palm of your hand.

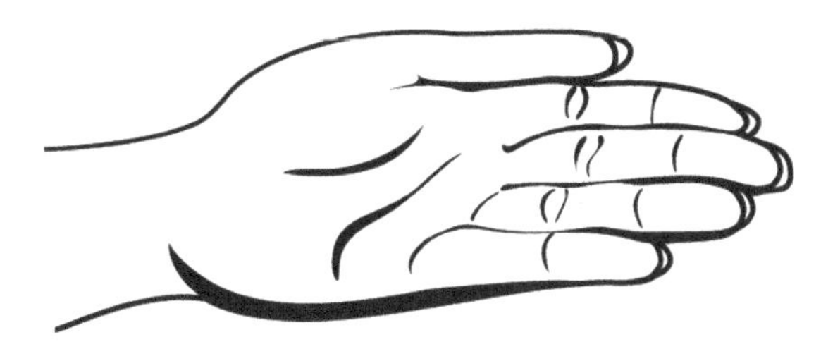

- Sticky Fig Breakfast Bowls
- NutriBullet Bircher
- Breakfast Bars
- Peanut Butter Granola Clusters
- Eggs Cocotte
- Clementine and Cranberry Compote
- Apple, Fig and Walnut Compote
- Breakfast Burritos
- Chia Seed Porridge/Pudding (Three Ways)
- Mushroom Toast, Avocado & Poached Egg
- Spinach Pancakes with Smoked Salmon & Cream Cheese
- Baked Beans on Toast
- Champ Farls and Poached Egg
- On the go Smoothies
    - Black Forest Breakfast Smoothie
    - Tropical On the Go Smoothie
    - My Favourite Breakfast Smoothie
- Quinoa Porridge
- Sweet Potato Breakfast Muffins
- Carrot Cake Breakfast Muffins

Key to recipes

 – 10 mins or less

 – Vegetarian  – Vegan  – Low FODMAP  – Dairy Free – Gluten Free

BREAKFAST

STICKY FIG BREAKFAST BOWLS

I'm not a fan of a fresh date... which I know is sacrilege to many people. Once they are cooked...even a little bit as in this recipe, I LOVE them. Figs and blackberries both come into season about the same time and if you are lucky you can forage for both. This feels like a really indulgent and quite posh breakfast, when in fact it's really just assembling some store cupboard staples.

Portion size

Serves 2

Cook time

Oven cook 10 minutes

- 2 large ripe figs
- ½ tsp ground cinnamon
- 1 tbsp runny honey
- 2 tbsp orange juice
- 50g blackberries
- 200g yogurt
- 2 heaped tbsp homemade granola
- 2 tsp mixed seeds

Heat the oven to 180°C

Quarter the figs, place in a heatproof dish.

Mix the cinnamon, honey and juice together and pour over the figs and then bake in the oven for 10 mins until soft and sticky. Scatter the blackberries over the figs and pop back in the oven while you begin to assemble the bowls.

Divide the yogurt into bowls, top with the warm sticky figs, scatter the granola and mixed seeds. Eat ASAP.

Tips & Hints

Alternative to figs could be apples/pears? Also, to make dairy-free swap dairy yogurt for coconut or soya yogurt. This recipe can also be gluten-free depending on the granola.

NUTRIBULLET BIRCHER

This is such a nutritious wholesome yet fabulously fast breakfast to prepare...but still guaranteed to keep you feeling satisfied all morning long. Normally Bircher muesli is made by soaking all the ingredients overnight which allows them to become more digestible. Sometimes you don't remember to do the soaking, or you just fancy the taste of Bircher when you get up. This is where this NutriBullet Bircher comes to the rescue.

Portion size

Makes one portion

Cook time

No cook

- 20g Oats
- 20g Quinoa Flakes
- 1 tbsp Chia Seeds
- 1 tbsp unsweetened desiccated coconut
- 60ml coconut milk
- 30 ml coconut water
- 20ml apple juice
- 1 tbsp yogurt
- 4 frozen strawberries

Add all the ingredient to your NutriBullet cup, blend until well combined.

Tips & Hints

Breakfasts are often more Carb based – the good thing about this Bircher is that it also contains Quinoa (a seed) flakes and chia seeds which are good sources of protein.

NUTTY CRANBERRY BREAKFAST BARS

In an ideal world we would all eat our breakfast sitting down at a table feeling calm and relaxed and settling into the new day. In real life you are just as likely to be rushing out the door already fully submerged in your "To Do List". These Breakfast Bars are perfect for those mornings...rather than leave yourself to the mercy of "I'll just grab something en-route"... which so often become coffee and a pastry. These Breakfast Bars are well balanced and a complete meal – just remember to eat sloooowwly... gobble this down thinking it's a flapjack and you'll be left wanting more.

Portion size

Makes 12 bars

Cook time

Stove top – 5 mins

Bake time – 15-20 mins

For the Date Paste

- 300g Dates
- ½ cup water

For the Breakfast Bars

- 125g Peanut Butter
- 50g Coconut Oil

Dry Ingredients

- 250g Rolled Oats (blitz 50g into oat flour)
- 50g Desiccated Coconut
- 1 dstsp ground flaxseed
- ½ tsp ground cinnamon
- Pinch sea salt
- 1 tbsp sunflower seeds
- 1 tbsp chia seeds
- 2 tbsp unblanched almonds
- 2 tbsp dried cranberry

Tips & Hints

Nuts and seeds are a good source of vegetable protein and contain the good fats – particularly omega 3; baking them also helps to make nuts and seeds more digestible meaning you absorb more of the nutrients.

Line a 9 x 13 inch baking tray with parchment paper.

Pre-heat the oven to 180°C

Make the date paste by cooking the dates and water in a large pan over a medium heat. The dates will start to soften after about 5 minutes. Mash them down with a fork until the dates begin to dissolve into a thick paste.

To make the breakfast bars. Add the nut butter and coconut oil to the date paste and mix well until thoroughly combined. Add in the dry ingredients leaving some almonds and cranberries to place on top before baking. Ensure the ingredients are well mixed. Pour the mix into your prepared tray and spread evenly. I find that a couple of quick taps of the tray on the counter top helps the mix settle. Sprinkle with remaining chopped almonds and cranberries.

Bake for 15–20 minutes. Allow to cool before cutting into even rectangles.

PEANUT BUTTER GRANOLA CLUSTERS

This is a great breakfast staple, a fabulous way to use up old black bananas which I'm using here to reduce the sugar content. I warn you that these Peanut Butter Clusters are just as moreish as those advertised on the TV... so stick to the portion size LOL!

Portion size

Makes 15 portions – can be kept in an airtight jar for 8 weeks.

Cook time

Bake time 1 hour

- 400g jumbo rolled oats
- 100g almonds, chopped
- 60g pumpkin seeds
- 60g sunflower seeds
- ½ teaspoon cinnamon
- Pinch of salt
- 80ml coconut oil, optional
- 80ml pure maple syrup
- 1 tsp vanilla extract
- 2 small ripe bananas, mashed (about 1 cup)
- 200g peanut butter
- 2 tsp mixed seeds

Preheat oven to 150°C

In a large bowl, mix together the oats, almonds, seeds, cinnamon and salt.

Warm your coconut oil and maple syrup, combine with vanilla extract.

Mash your bananas and measure your nut butter. Combine the wet ingredients with the oat mixture.

Toss and mix to coat well.

Spread mixture evenly on a lined or lightly greased baking sheet (I used two baking sheets). You can either lightly compact the mixture or loosely spread it out a bit. If compacting, you'll want to mix the granola when rotating after 30 minutes.

Bake for 30 minutes. Turn and rotate sheet/ sheets, bake an additional 25–30 minutes. Keep an eye towards the end so it doesn't over brown (ovens run differently). Remove from oven, granola will be somewhat soft at first. Leave to cool for 15 minutes, break up into chunks, especially the centre part if you've compacted the mixture. Let granola cool completely to harden.

Tips & Hints

Oats provide good fibre which makes for optimum gut function.

EGGS COCOTTE

This is a lovely weekend breakfast when you have a bit more time. It feels rich and indulgent. Make the leeks up to a couple of days before and store in an airtight container in the fridge then just decant into your pots on the morning you want to eat. Watch out for hot spots in your oven as you might want to turn your tray halfway through cooking to prevent overcooking the eggs.

Eggs en Cocotte with sautéed leeks and Soldiers.

Portion size

Serves 2

Cook time

Bake time – 15 mins

- 60g leeks, chopped
- Handful of fresh chopped spinach
- 2 large eggs
- Salt and pepper to season
- 2 heaped tbsp half fat crème fraiche
- 2 slices rye bread
- 2 tsp Salmon Eggs
- Fresh dill

Pre-heat the oven to 180°C, gas mark 4 and put a kettle on to boil.

Gently steam the leeks with some seasoning in its own juices in a small pan with a lid for 5 minutes, then add the chopped spinach and allow to wilt. Divide the cooked leek and spinach mix between two ramekins and place them in a roasting tin then break an egg into each ramekin, add some more seasoning, then put a tablespoon of crème fraîche on top of each yolk. Place the roasting tin on the centre shelf of the oven and pour enough hot water, from the kettle, into the tin to come halfway up the sides of the dishes. Now let the eggs bake for 15 minutes if you like them soft and runny, or 18 minutes if you like them more set.

Serve on rye bread toast topped with the salmon eggs and some fresh dill.

Tips & Hints

Eggs are a complete source of protein meaning they contain all the essential amino acids that the body can't make for itself and are a good breakfast choice as keep you fuller for longer.

CLEMENTINE AND CRANBERRY COMPOTE

This dish was inspired by a breakfast I had during a trip home to Northern Ireland. My B&B had award winning breakfast and there was an autumnal fruit compote on a very comprehensive menu. They served it with a Hazelnut yogurt; I'm not a fan of flavoured yoghurts as many tend to have a lot of added sugar so serve mine with a gorgeous natural yogurt as there is more than enough sweetness in the compote.

Portion size

Serves 4

Cook time

Stove top cook time – 15 mins

- 5 clementines
- 60 g frozen cranberries (defrosted)
- 1tsp honey

Zest one clementine. Peel and segment the clementines. Cut each segment in half. Place one third to one side. Place the remaining clementine into a small saucepan with the grated zest, the defrosted cranberries and honey. Gently warm for about 10 minutes. Add the remaining clementines and cook for a further 5 mins.

Serve with natural yogurt, mixed seeds, nuts or granola.

Tips & Hints

Cranberries are high in antioxidants which reduce the "rusting" of our cells and soak up free radicals which can cause damage. Cranberries are particularly good for skin health, blood health along with boosting the immune system.

APPLE, FIG AND WALNUT COMPOTE

This compote was created in our French Retreat venue where we have both apple and fig trees in the back garden. Anyone with fruit trees knows that there are times when you literally have a glut of fruit. This compote freezes well so make it in autumn and you can enjoy all winter.

Portion size

Serves 8 portions

Cook time

20 mins

- 4 granny smith apples, peeled and chopped
- 350g fresh figs, quartered
- 1 tsp mixed spice
- 65g coconut sugar
- 40g walnuts, chopped

Place the apple, figs, spice and sugar in a deep pot and gently bring up to a boil. Stirring regularly. Cook for 15 minutes, add the walnuts and take off the heat.

Serve with natural yogurt, mixed seeds, nuts or granola.

Tips & Hints

The benefit of walnuts is that they contain fibre, antioxidants, omega 3, all of which are good for brain health and gut health.

BREAKFAST BURRITOS

These Breakfast Burritos were originally made for our Sugar Detox Retreat. We exclude all grains and fruit on that retreat and so I have to be creative with breakfasts. If you make up the fillings the night before and keep in an airtight container then in the morning you need only rustle up the omelette...which will take you about 2–3 minutes. A couple of minutes more on assembling your burrito and you have a delicious protein rich breakfast done.

It's no secret that we love eggs for breakfast here at The Body Retreat. What's not to love – they are quick, simple to prepare and lend themselves to so many creative recipes.

Here we have taken the idea of a Mexican burrito wrap, with the tastes of cool avocado, juicy tomatoes and spicy chilli and given a little Conscious Cooking twist.

Using egg omelette in place of the wrap you can create a taste sensation.

You will notice in the ingredients that I use the leaves from the celery – most people chop these off and discard them; not us. Have you ever tried them? The taste is fabulous, I always keep them for soups, stocks, even making my own celery salt. But here I like them as they add a bright fresh oniony herby flavour. Most people when you serve the burrito will not notice the celery taste but will enjoy the extra something it brings to the dish. Try it and see for yourself.

Portion size

Serves 8

Cook time

20 mins

- ½ ripe Avocado
- 1 inch piece cucumber, cubed
- 2 cherry tomatoes, halved
- 1 spring onion, chopped
- Handful baby spinach, roughly chopped
- Handful fresh coriander, roughly chopped
- Celery leaves, roughly chopped
- ¼ fresh red chilli, finely chopped
- Juice of ½ lime
- 2 Medium Eggs
- 1 tsp butter
- Salt and black pepper

First make up the salsa filling: combine all the ingredients except the eggs and butter in a bowl, season and put to one side while you make up the egg pancake.

To make the pancakes, beat the eggs and season with salt and pepper; heat the butter in a small shallow frying pan. Add the eggs and cook for about 2–3 minutes until firm.

To construct your breakfast burrito, simply slide the egg pancake onto a large plate, spoon the salsa in a line through the centre from edge to edge. Roll up to make your burrito. I like to serve my Breakfast Burrito with a dessert spoon each of tomato salsa, Guacamole and Sour Cream.

Tips & Hints

Eggs do contain cholesterol, but we do need cholesterol particularly for our hormones and keeping them balanced.

CHIA SEED PORRIDGE/ PUDDING (THREE WAYS)

Is it a pudding?? Or is it a porridge???

I suppose the cold versions are technically a pudding but I don't really like to use the term pudding at breakfast. Call them whatever you like...these little pots are delicious and a fabulous way to start your day. Protein rich, this a breakfast to enjoy when you really need some serious sustained energy all morning.

Chia seeds are best eaten soaked – they retain up to 8 times their normal weight in water. This means they are super hydrating for the body.

Portion size

Each recipe makes one portion

Cook time

No cook

Tips & Hints

Chia seeds are power seeds which contain omega 3 oils which are anti-inflammatory and a good source of protein as they contain all 9 amino acids and fibre for digestion – all of which help to balance blood sugar.

Chia Seed Porridge with Apple & Berries

- 35gm Chia Seed
- 1 tsp Flaxseed
- 1 Cup Nut Milk
- 1 Apple Grated
- ¼ Vanilla Pod.
- ½ cup berries
- 20ml apple juice
- 1 tbsp yogurt

4 frozen strawberries Mix the seeds, milk, apple and vanilla together with a splash of water and cover and leave in the fridge overnight.

In the morning before you eat, remove the vanilla pod, loosen off with a splash of unsweetened unroasted almond milk or coconut water. Top with your berries and enjoy.

Tropical Chia Seed Porridge

- 20g Mango, chopped
- ½ small banana chopped
- 1 Cup Full Fat Coconut Milk
- 35g Chia Seed
- 1 tsp Flaxseed
- 1 passion fruit

Puree the mango and banana with the coconut milk. Mix with the seeds and a splash of water, mix well and cover and leave in the fridge overnight.

In the morning loosen off the mix with coconut water if necessary and top with the fresh passion fruit seeds.

Chai Spiced Chia Seed Porridge

- 35g Chia Seeds
- 1 tsp ground flaxseed
- 1 cup almond milk
- 1 cardamom pod
- Pinch ground cinnamon
- Pinch ground ginger
- Pinch ground nutmeg

Mix all ingredients with a splash of water, mix well and cover, and leave in the fridge overnight. Remove the cardamom pod, loosen with coconut milk if necessary.

MUSHROOM TOAST, AVOCADO & POACHED EGG

I feel silly calling this dish a recipe, as to be honest it's really just assembling. But it is assembling three very delicious things. I often serve this on retreat when I have a retreater who is gluten or grain free as the mushroom makes a fantastic bread alternative.

All we are doing is replacing the regular slice of toast with a portabella mushroom... it works a charm. Makes for a very filling and satisfying dish. In fact, the amount of oohs and ahhs that go up from the breakfast table when this dish is presented to the lucky retreaters makes me think that we should ditch the bready version altogether.

Try it...you won't be disappointed, and it is so easy to make it hardly warrants being called a recipe.

Portion size

Makes one portion

Cook time

0–15 minutes

- 1 large Portabella Mushroom
- ¼ tsp rapeseed oil
- ½ Avocado
- Juice of a lemon
- 1 Large Egg
- Salt and black pepper

Before we begin, first let me share my top mushroom related tip... never wash your mushrooms!! They are porous and will soak up the water making for a very flaccid and unappetising mushroom. Firstly, start with an organic mushroom, next give it a dust/brush, you can use a special mushroom brush or you can do as I do and use some kitchen paper.

Remove all obvious signs of muck and dirt, give the mushroom a gentle tap on a chopping board to remove any resistant dirt and you are ready to cook.

To cook your mushroom, preheat your oven to 170°C. Lightly grease a baking tray, I normally use a baking brush to brush a thin veil of rapeseed oil. Place your mushroom cap side down on the baking tray and pop in the hot oven for about 10–15 minutes (depending on how big your mushroom is)...you want the mushroom to have softened but not disintegrated.

Meanwhile mash up your avocado with a squeeze of fresh lemon and a quick grind of black pepper. Set to one side.

Next poach your egg to whatever texture you like; personally I always go for a soft poach so that you get gooey egg yolk as sauce.

Poaching an egg is simple: I first crack an egg onto a saucer making it easier to slide into the pan; bring a pan of water to the boil – you want it to be about 5cm deep and add a drop of vinegar. Stir the water to create a bit of a whirlpool and slide the egg into the centre, so the white wraps itself around the yolk. Then cook for 4-5 minutes on a low heat until the white is cooked. Then lift out with a slotted spoon.

Now to assemble it couldn't be more simple: place your mushroom cap side down on a plate, fill the cup with avocado and then plonk the egg on top. A quick salt and black pepper and you are ready to serve. You'll want to eat this immediately.

Tips & Hints

The benefits of mushrooms are that they contain protein and fibre. The micronutrients (B vitamins and selenium) help to keep the immune system healthy.

SPINACH PANCAKES WITH SMOKED SALMON & CREAM CHEESE

No way could I have a recipe book without a pancake recipe. I think there are 3 or 4 others on the blog, as well as in the first Conscious Cooking Book. We serve pancakes on every retreat...even the Sugar Detox Retreat!! People think that pancakes are naughty – I suppose because often when we think of pancakes we think of a big old stack of American style pancakes dripping with syrup.

But pancakes are so much more, they are so versatile and with a few tweaks can be a really healthy addition to your weekly meal plans. While I do love a sweet pancake, these savoury pancakes are also a real winner.

Portion size

Makes one portion

Cook time

Stove top cooking – 3-4 minutes

- 100g spinach
- 2 eggs – separated
- 200 ml milk

Dry ingredients:

- 125g buckwheat flour
- 1 tsp baking powder
- Pinch of nutmeg
- Pinch sea salt
- 1 tbsp rapeseed oil for frying
- 100g smoked salmon
- 100g cream cheese

Wash and dry the spinach and then place in a blender with the egg yolks and milk. Blitz until smooth. Mix the dry ingredients in a large bowl and then stir in the milk mixture.

Whisk the egg whites and then fold into the mix.

Heat a little oil in a frying pan over a medium heat and pour ladle spoons of the batter into the pan.

Cook for 3-4 minutes on each side before turning over with a spatula and cooking the other side.

Keep warm in a low oven until you're ready to serve them with smoked salmon and cream cheese.

Tips & Hints

1. To make dairy-free – swap to dairy-free milks and cream cheese alternative. Cashew cream is also useful here – see recipe.
2. Can be kept in the fridge for a couple of days once cool or freeze with a sheet of greaseproof paper in between each one to stop them sticking.

BAKED BEANS ON TOAST

Baked Beans on toast...such a staple of many a breakfast table... or lunch table or even supper table. There is no bad time to enjoy this protein-rich dish. However, you do want to avoid the store-bought canned beans as they contain high amounts of sugar and/or artificial sweeteners.

Make a double batch of these beans and freeze in individual portions so they are ready to go for a very quick bite any time of the day or evening. They can be frozen and kept in the freezer for up to 12 weeks.

Portion size

6 Servings

Cook time

Stove top cooking 5-10minutes

- 2 tsp rapeseed oil
- 1 small onion, finely chopped
- 1 small stick celery, finely chopped
- 1 clove garlic, finely chopped
- 1 tsp tomato puree
- 1 tin of good quality tinned tomatoes
- A few sprigs of thyme
- A pinch dried chilli flakes
- ½ tsp smoked paprika
- 1 x400g can cannellini beans, drained
- 1 x 400g butter beans

Heat the oil in a non-stick pan, then gently fry the onion and celery for 5-10 minutes until the onions and celery are softened and just starting to turn golden. For the last minute add in the garlic, then add the puree and brown sugar. Stir in the tomatoes, stock, thyme and chilli flakes and seasoning to taste, then simmer the sauce for 5 mins. Add the beans, then simmer for another 5 mins until the sauce has thickened.

Serve the beans with a slice of toast.

Tips & Hints

You may think that it is much easier to reach for a tin of baked beans – but this recipe is so quick and simple and once you've tasted them you will never go back!

CHAMP FARLS AND POACHED EGG

My love for the humble potato knows no bounds; mind you, as an Irish woman it's in my DNA. It gets such a bad rap compared with its Sweet Potato cousin. But there is no reason to ditch the white potato.

This dish combines two Northern Irish kitchen staples. The potato farl – the word farl originates from the Gaelic word fardel meaning four parts. These potato griddle breads are often made with leftover mashed potato and are served as part of an Ulster Fry. Champ is made by combining mashed potatoes and chopped scallions (spring onions) with butter and milk; this is most often served as a main course side. Both of these are a lovely thing...combined together and they become food of the gods... I did admit a bias, didn't I???

This makes a great weekend breakfast dish when topped with a soft poached egg, and I like to add a dollop of sauerkraut on the side.

Portion size

Makes 4 Champ Farls

Cook time

10–15 minutes

Tips & Hints

Leaving the skins on the potatoes means you get the best of the micronutrients (B vitamins, vitamin C, iron and calcium along with others!) that are there and it also helps to boost the amount of fibre.

- 1 Spring onion, chopped. Include the green.
- 2 tbsp milk of choice
- 2 Cups of Left-over Mashed Potato, with skins on please
- 2 tbsp Flour, I use buckwheat flour
- 1 dstsp Butter, melted
- Salt and Freshly ground black pepper

To serve – soft poached egg and sauerkraut

First cook the spring onion in the milk for 2–3 minutes until just soft.

Place mashed potato in medium bowl. Stir in flour, salt and melted butter. Mix lightly until dough forms. Add in the cooked spring onions and a little of the cooking milk if your dough is too firm.

On a well-floured surface, knead the dough lightly. The dough will be sticky. Use a floured rolling pin to flatten into a 9-inch circle about ¼ inch thick. Cut into quarters using a floured knife.

Add ½ tsp rapeseed oil in a heavy bottom frying pan and cook the farls for 3 minutes on each side or until evenly browned. Pop into the oven for 10–15 minutes until piping hot all through.

ON THE GO SMOOTHIES

No Time!!! It's the number one reason we hear on retreat why women are not eating breakfast. The truth is that starting your day off well doesn't have to mean chopping, stirring or cooking.

These On the Go Smoothies take minutes to prepare and even better they can be made up the night before so you literally have to grab and go. Meaning that there really is no excuse to not break your fast in a healthy way.

Portion size

Each recipe makes one portion

Cook time

No cook

The Base

- 25g Jumbo Rolled Oats
- 1 tsp Ground Flaxseed
- 1 Dstsp Nut Butter
- 1 Dstsp Yogurt of choice
- 1 cup Nut milk of choice
- ½ cup coconut water

To make – add all ingredients to a NutriBullet and blend.

Black Forest Breakfast Smoothie

Let me start by confessing that I'm not a fan of chocolate at breakfast in any form. Partly that's a personal preference and partly it's because I feel that chocolate is a treat and by the nature of treats, they should be occasional and not a part of your daily diet. So, for me this Black Forest Breakfast Smoothie is a special occasion breakfast. It is rich and indulgent and you honestly won't believe that it is healthy... but please...don't start having these every morning!!!!

Black Forest On the Go

To your base add:

- 1 palmful of frozen dark cherries
- 1tsp organic cocoa powder
- Top with ½ tsp raw Cocoa nibs

To make – add all ingredients to a NutriBullet and blend.

Tips & Hints

Smoothies are great because if you add the right balance of ingredients you can get a balanced meal of fat, fibre, protein and carbohydrates.

My Favourite Breakfast Smoothie

I've spent so long following certain programmes to help correct poor gut health. This has meant following exclusion diets. During these times I would often make this breakfast smoothie. I use strawberries as they are low in fructose, green banana as they are also low in fructose but also higher in potassium than their yellow counterpart. Coconut milk and yogurt as I've been dairy free for years, but you could use a full fat organic dairy alternative. Add in the nut butter for protein and ground flaxseed for fibre and you have a winning, well-balanced breakfast to go. Top tip is to freeze your bananas and strawberries as soon as you return from the store; this adds a lovely creaminess to the smoothie and also means that you will also always have the ingredients ready for a smoothie all year round.

My Favourite On the Go

To your base add:

- ½ green banana
- 1 palmful frozen strawberries

To make – add all ingredients to a NutriBullet and blend.

Tropical On the Go Smoothie

On the Go Smoothie…these are perfect to prepare the night before and leave in the beaker for a quick grab and go breakfast choice. They take only a few moments to prepare. The original version of this On the Go Smoothie is a Banana Peanut Butter version (you can find this on our Conscious Cooking Blog) but sometimes it's nice to ring the changes and especially during the summer months I love the bright zingy taste of the tropical fruits in this version.

Tropical On the Go

To your base add:

- 1 Slice pineapple
- ¼ Ripe Mango
- Top with ½ Passion fruit

To make – add all ingredients to a NutriBullet and blend.

QUINOA PORRIDGE

Have you tried quinoa at breakfast time yet? It makes a surprisingly creamy porridge making it ideal for a heart-warming and healthy breakfast. If you have never used quinoa for breakfast, give this hot quinoa cereal recipe a try. It is a great alternative to your usual oat breakfast and an easy way to get in a healthy dose of plant-based protein into your diet in the morning.

Porridge is such a breakfast staple for many households, but all too often it's made with quick cook oats, skimmed milk and loaded with fruit and syrups. Not the most balanced of breakfasts and very likely to leave you wanting a little something about 11am. Just a few tweaks are all you need to turn porridge into a protein packed power porridge (in fact there is just such a recipe on the Conscious Cooking Blog). If you are looking to exclude grains from your daily diet, then Quinoa Porridge is a great alternative. It has a very nutty taste and texture...it does absorb a lot of liquid, but the result is a creamy delicious wholesome bowl of yumminess.

If you want to double batch this porridge and keep a portion for later in the week, place it in an airtight container and keep in the fridge up to 3 days. When ready to serve, add a few tablespoons of water (or coconut milk) before reheating on the stove top or in the microwave.

Portion size

Serves 1

Cook time

15–20 mins

To make one generous portion

- 50g Tri Colour Quinoa
- 150ml Coconut milk
- 50ml of water
- 1 tsp maple syrup or honey

To make, place all the ingredients in a small pot and stir well, bring up to a quick and rolling boil, stirring constantly. Turn down the heat and continue to cook for about 15–20 minutes until the quinoa is al-dente. Top with seeds and nuts of your choice.

Top tip... you can reduce the cooking time by soaking the ingredients in the pan overnight.

Tips & Hints

Quinoa is actually a seed so it is considered a protein and carbohydrate, helping to balance blood sugar and keep you fuller for longer.

SWEET POTATO BREAKFAST MUFFINS

The Body Retreat is full of busy professional women...both the team and the retreaters... busy women who want to make better choices about the food that they eat but who also have to balance the demands of a busy lifestyle.

So, while I'd love it if every retreater made time to sit and enjoy a relaxed breakfast, I know there are days when that genuinely isn't possible. There are days when you need to grab and go. On these days then our On the Go Smoothies are a great option. But if you don't even have time to bung a few things in the blender than the next best option is a grab and go breakfast muffin. These muffins are nutritiously dense and well balanced and a much better choice that those sold at your local coffee house. Make up a batch and get them in the freezer... then on those hectic mornings just grab a muffin, pop in your handbag and let it defrost while you go about your day.

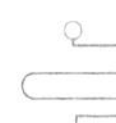

Portion size

Makes 8 big muffins

Cook time

15–20 mins

Wet Ingredients:

- 150g sweet potato puree
- 1 cup banana puree
- 75g nut butter
- 3 large eggs

Dry Ingredients:

- 30g coconut flour
- 30 g jumbo oats – plus extra for topping
- 30g chopped walnuts
- 1 tsp baking powder
- 1 tsp ground flaxseed
- Pinch sea salt

Preheat oven to 180°C

Bake the sweet potatoes, scoop out the flesh and mash into a puree. Mash the bananas into a puree then mix the wet ingredients and the dry ingredients separately. Mix together to form a batter. Sprinkle with oats and bake for 15–20 minutes until a toothpick comes out clean and dry.

Tips & Hints

Sweet potatoes and bananas are a good alternative to sugar in baking.

CARROT CAKE BREAKFAST MUFFINS

The Body Retreat is full of busy professional women...both the team and the retreaters... busy women who want to make better choices about the food that they eat but who also have to balance the demands of a busy lifestyle.

Portion size

Makes 12 muffins

Cook time

15-20 mins

Wet Ingredients:

- 4 eggs
- 100ml rapeseed oil
- 100g apple sauce
- 50ml maple syrup
- 1 tsp vanilla extract

Dry Ingredients:

- 100g wholegrain flour
- 50g whole jumbo oats
- 25g ground flaxseed
- 25g chia seeds
- 1tsp baking powder
- Pinch sea salt
- 2 tsp cinnamon
- ½ tsp ground nutmeg
- ½ tsp allspice
- 100g freshly grated carrots
- 50g chopped walnuts

Preheat the oven to 180°C

Beat all the wet ingredients together. Mix in the remaining dry ingredients, folding in the grated carrot and walnuts last. Fill 12 pre-lined cupcake cases and bake for 15-20 minutes until a toothpick comes out clean.

Tips & Hints

Carrots are a good source of beta-carotene, fibre and antioxidants.

- Beetroot, Butterbean, Feta and Mint Salad
- Mexican Bean Salad
- Kale, squash, pomegranate and Halloumi Salad
- Chicken, Fennel & Orange Salad
- Rainbow Bowl
- Chicken & Tomato Bowl

Key to recipes

 – 10 mins or less

 – Vegetarian  – Vegan – Low FODMAP  – Dairy Free – Gluten Free

SALADS

HOW TO MAKE A SALAD

When I was growing up, salad was always exactly the same things – a slice of bright pink ham, a boiled egg, iceberg lettuce, tomato, cucumber, spring onions and salad cream on the side. I bet your mouth is watering right now at the sound of this taste sensation LOL! Despite this inauspicious introduction to salads, I do love, love, love salads. However, I do despair of how boring they can be. I make a lot of salad both on retreat and at home and am so surprised when people say "I'd never think of using xxx" or "your salads are always so much tastier" ... if you are bored of salad then let me show you the path towards salad nirvana.

The key to a salad for me is texture and colour...and of course flavour. But I make sure that in each bowl or plate I'm aiming to have a variety of complementing and contrasting colours and textures. It makes for a much more interesting mouthful and so therefore a much more conscious eating experience.

All salads start with a leafy base – rocket, spinach, kale, cabbage, greens. You are spoilt for choice. Next you build up with your fibre veggies, so think cucumber, celery, courgette, peppers, broccoli, radish. Next it's time for some starch, so think carrot, squash, corn, rice, barley. Now we want protein, so think chicken, beef, tofu, tuna, hummus, beans and pulses. Now I like a little sweetness – think tomato, pomegranate, sweet peas, pear, apple, apricot. Finally, I want some fat. Some delicious cold pressed rapeseed oil, extra virgin olive oil, a sprinkle of seeds or nuts or even a little cheese.

SALAD DRESSINGS

A great salad deserves a little dressing to bring all the flavours together. Here are two of my favourite Salad Dressings.

Simple Salad Dressing

- Rapeseed Oil
- Raw Apple Cider Vinegar
- Sea Salt
- Freshly Ground Black Pepper

Orange Mustard Salad Dressing

- Rapeseed Oil
- Balsamic Vinegar
- Juice of half Fresh Orange
- ½ tsp coarse ground mustard
- Sea Salt
- Freshly Ground Black Pepper

SAVOURY (OR SWEET!) CASHEW CREAM

Portion size

1 dessert spoon

Cook time

No cook

- 1 cup (150g) raw cashews
- ½–¾ cup (125–190 ml) filtered water (add more water according to consistency desired)

Savoury Cashew Cream

- Juice of ½ lemon
- ½ tsp. Sea salt
- ½ tsp apple cider vinegar (optional)
- 1 garlic clove (optional)
- 1 tbsp olive oil (optional)

Sweet Cashew Cream

- 2–4 tbsp honey or pure maple syrup
- ½ tsp vanilla extract

Soak the cashews in filtered water for 3 hrs or more then strain.

Add the cashews and fresh filtered water (½–¾ cup) to the blender or food processor and blend until smooth.

Add remaining ingredients depending on whether you are making a sweet or savoury cream, then blend until smooth.

Savoury Cashew Cream

Can be used as a pizza topping, as a healthy pasta dish, or over vegetables, baked dishes, casseroles, healthy Mexican meals, as a salad dressing (this can be thinned down with extra olive oil) or anywhere where you may have added a savoury creamy sauce!

Sweet Cashew Cream

Can be drizzled over fruit and healthy desserts.

Tips & Hints

Cashew nuts contain monounsaturated fatty acid and higher amounts of HDL good cholesterol which is good for brain health. Magnesium helps protect against high blood pressure.

BEETROOT, BUTTERBEAN, FETA AND MINT SALAD

Portion size

Serves 2

Cook time

No cook

Salad:

- 2 handfuls rocket leaves
- 2 small beetroots – cooked and cubed
- 400g butterbeans, drained and rinsed
- 2 ripe tomatoes, cubed
- 30g black olives
- ½ red onion, sliced
- Small handful fresh mint leaves
- 100g feta

Dressing:

- 1 tbsp rapeseed oil
- 1 lemon
- Salt and black pepper

Mix all the ingredients and divide between two plates.

Make the dressing by mixing the oil with the juice of the lemon, season with salt and black pepper and pour over the salad.

Enjoy asap.

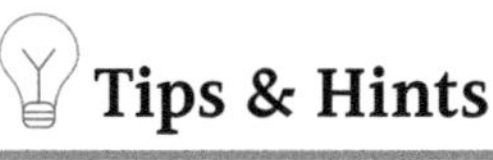

Tips & Hints

Don't just think salads are for summer; they are good all year round and the great thing about them is that you can prepare them the night before and take to work the next day, providing a healthy nutritious lunch option.

MEXICAN BEAN SALAD

Portion size

Serves 2

Cook time

No cook

Salad:

- 50g frozen sweetcorn (defrosted)
- 1 head romaine lettuce, roughly chopped
- 75g cooked black beans
- 6 cherry tomatoes, quartered
- ¼ cucumber, chopped
- 2 Spring onions, chopped
- ½ ripe avocado, chopped
- Handful chopped parsley
- Handful chopped coriander

Dressing:

- ½ jalapeno, chopped
- 1 tbsp rapeseed oil
- Squeeze lemon & lime juice
- Salt & Pepper

Combine all the salad ingredients together in a large bowl.

In a small jug or mug combine the dressing ingredients.

Drizzle the dressing over the salad before serving.

I like to serve this salad with a generous dessert spoon of the savoury cashew cream, it adds flavour, extra protein... and it's just so delicious.

Tips & Hints

When making salads it is good to think about colour, texture and adding flavours! Variety is the spice of life!

KALE, SQUASH, POMEGRANATE AND HALLOUMI SALAD

The combination of sweet squash, salty halloumi, and hearty kale just goes so well together; this is a fabulous autumnal or winter salad as the kale suits the seasons more than crisp cold leaves.

Portion size

Makes Two Generous Salads

Cook time

25 mins

Salad:

- ½ medium butternut squash
- 2 dstsp rapeseed oil
- Mixed herbs
- Two large handfuls of fresh kale leaves
- Salt
- 2 dstsp Pomegranate seeds
- 1 tbsp mixed seeds
- 1 tbsp walnut halves
- 2 tbsp defrosted peas
- 1 spring onion, chopped
- 150g Halloumi Cheese

Vinaigrette:

- 2 dstsp rapeseed oil
- 1 tsp apple cider vinegar
- Garlic
- Salt and black pepper

Note: you can make all the component parts in advance and serve this salad cold, but there is something really special about warm squash and cheese on the cold leaves.

Preheat the oven to 180°C. Peel and dice butternut squash into large bite sized chunks. Place the squash in a baking tray, and drizzle with rapeseed oil, mixed herbs and a pinch of salt. Roast in the oven for about 20 minutes until the butternut is soft enough to put a fork through it without resistance.

Add kale to a salad bowl and sprinkle with a pinch of sea salt, Massage the kale to break down the fibre and soften the leaves. Make a quick vinaigrette by adding rapeseed oil, apple cider vinegar, garlic and salt and black pepper to a small container with a lid. Shake well to combine. Drizzle the kale with a generous amount of the vinaigrette. Massage the kale once more and then set aside until you ready to assemble the dish.

Meanwhile, dry fry or grill sliced halloumi until golden on both sides. This usually takes about 4–5 minutes. Serve in slices or cut into smaller pieces.

Add other ingredients to the kale then top with roasted butternut squash and halloumi and serve!

Tips & Hints

Halloumi cheese has a higher melting point making it a great choice to heat up.

CHICKPEA, FENNEL & ORANGE SALAD

This is a bit of a taste explosion, fragrant fennel, sweet orange, salty olives, crunchy nuts, fresh parsley...I love this salad on a warm day. It is so light and tasty.

Portion size

Serves 2

Cook time

No cook

Salad:

- 2 handfuls baby spinach leaves
- ½ bulb fennel, very thinly sliced
- ½ orange, segmented
- 2 dstsp chopped almonds
- 1 dstsp mixed seeds
- 1 dstsp black olives
- ½ can chickpeas, rinsed and drained
- 1 sml handful fresh parsley, chopped

Dressing:

- 1 tbsp rapeseed oil
- 1 tsp wholegrain mustard
- Juice of ½ orange

So simple, the trick here is to make sure that your veggies are very thinly sliced...if you are not confident in your knife skills then it's worth using a mandolin (always use the handguard and go slow!!!) to achieve nice thin slices.

To construct your salad, place your leaves on the plate and then scatter on the remaining ingredients. Make up a simple dressing using the rapeseed, mustard and the juice of the remaining half orange and pour over.

Tips & Hints

Chickpeas are a great source of vegetable protein to add to salads.

RAINBOW BOWL

As the name suggests this salad bowl is all about eating the rainbow...in every single delicious mouthful. Fresh veggies and fruits, mixed with grains, pulses, nuts and seeds.

This is my favourite version of rainbow bowl... feel free to play around and make changes to make this your perfect bowl. If you don't like spinach, switch to rocket, if you don't like mango add pear, switch the wild rice for quinoa. Just keep the proportions the same and you're all good.

Portion size

Serves 1

Cook time

No cook

Salad:

- 1 handful baby spinach leaves
- 1 spring onion, chopped
- ½ medium carrot, grated
- 3-4 broccoli florets, roughly chopped
- ¼ red pepper, sliced
- 60g Whole Grain Basmati and Wild Rice Mix
- 60g black beans (cooked and cooled)
- 25g unblanched almonds, chopped
- 15g sunflower seeds
- ¼ mango, cubed
- Handful fresh parsley, roughly chopped

Dressing:

- 1 tsp tahini
- 1 tsp natural yogurt
- 1 dstsp rapeseed oil
- Big squeeze fresh lemon juice
- Salt and black pepper
- Fresh garlic grated

To make up your Rainbow bowl, unlike the other salads, you don't combine the ingredients, rather you place them all in the bowl in individual groups. So, place your greens to one side, place the carrots beside the green, then the red pepper etc, etc.

Now it's the dressing that bring this all together... you could make up a simple vinaigrette ... but I like to make a spicy tahini dressing.

To make the dressing mix the ingredients together. Now trust me here...this is going to look awful as you start to mix...but vigorously mix together until it goes past the stage of looking split and comes back together as a silky-smooth dressing. Dollop this on the middle of your plate and dip all your rainbow delights in.

Tips & Hints

Eating the rainbow means you are getting a wide range of plant-based goodness.

CHICKEN AND TOMATO BARLEY BOWL

Portion size

Serves 2

Cook time

No cook

Salad:

- 2 handful soft green leaves
- 2 cooked chicken breasts, sliced
- 2 slices Parma ham, sliced
- 100g fresh green beans – cooked al-dente, cooled and chopped
- 60g Pot Barley – cooked al-dente and cooled
- 25g pine nuts, freshly toasted
- 50g Sundried tomatoes
- 1 spring onion, sliced
- Handful fresh basil, chopped

Dressing:

- 1 dtsp balsamic vinegar
- 1 dstp Olive Oil
- ¼ tsp Dijon mustard
- Salt and black pepper

Place the leaves in the bottom of two large bowls and then top with equal amounts of the remaining ingredients. Top with the dressing and enjoy.

Tips & Hints

What is pot barley? It is where the whole grain barley has had the outer fibral hull removed in a shorter process compared to pearl barley. Pot barley provides fibre which help digestion and feeds the gut bacteria, it is low in cholesterol and helps balance blood sugar.

- Cauliflower, Chicken and Turmeric Soup
- Cauliflower Cheese Soup
- Lentil and Carrot Soup
- Gazpacho
- Broccoli, Cashews and Dill Soup
- Chinese Style Chicken & Sweetcorn Soup

Key to recipes

 – 10 mins or less

 – Vegetarian  – Vegan  – Low FODMAP  – Dairy Free – Gluten Free

SOUPS

HOW TO MAKE A SOUP

How much do I love soup... let me count the ways. I love how it's a one pot wonder, less washing up gets a big Heart from me. I love the different textures, silky smooth or big and chunky. I love how you can taste as you go along adding in little tweaks – soup making is not an exact science so keep tasting and keep tweaking. I love how a big bowl of soup can be like a warm hug in winter or a cool you down in summer.

A word about freshness. While vegetables that are just a little bit past their prime (such as bendy celery or carrots that are a bit bruised) are fine, if anything is REALLY old and looks terrible then it's best to bin those. Likewise, if anything smells particularly strong (cabbage for example) then that smell will translate into the flavour of your soup. I'm all for minimising waste but I'd much rather that you planned to use your vegetables before they were on the turn, so you are maximising your nutritional intake.

No matter the kind, all soups follow a similar path to deliciousness: the main ingredients of vegetables, proteins, fats go into a large pot along with your aromatics, herbs and spices, liquid is added and the whole thing is simmered until done.

Stock or Broth?

Most soups will ask you to add a liquid of some sort, often a stock. On retreat we use Marigold Veg Bouillon for our vegetable soups and bone broths for our meat and fish based soups. So why the difference?

Stock is water simmered with vegetables, aromatics, and sometimes cooked animal bones and sometimes with some meat still attached. It is cooked for a medium period of time—usually 4 to 6 hours—then strained.

On the other hand, Bone Broth is made from raw bones, but there can sometimes be some meat still attached. It is cooked for a long period of time—often more than 24 hours—and the goal is not only to extract the gelatine from the bones, but also to release the nutritious compounds and minerals (namely collagen, but also glucosamine, amino acids, electrolytes, calcium, and more.

Other flavoursome Liquids. Tinned tomato, coconut milk, miso, even fruit juice can all be added to a soup to give both flavour and increase liquid content of your soup.

Tips & Hints

Soups can help to warm and soften the stomach, being high in fluids they nourish our cells and skin; they can be healthy and nutritious, add fibre and preserve the nutritional value of the ingredients. They are rich in taste and by providing fullness are a great way for watching portion control.

CAULIFLOWER, CHICKEN AND TURMERIC SOUP

This is one of my favourite soups...especially if you need a big bowl of warming, immune boosting deliciousness.

Portion size

Serves 4

Cook time

40 minutes

- 1dstsp Coconut Oil
- 1 small onion, diced
- 1 leek, diced
- ½ clove garlic, crushed
- 1 stick Lemongrass
- 1 tsp ground Coriander
- 1 tsp ground Turmeric
- Zest of 1 lemon
- 1 Bay leaf
- Sea Salt and White pepper
- 4 chicken thighs
- 1 ltr chicken bone broth
- 40g mixed quinoa
- 1 small head of cauliflower, chopped up small
- 1 potato, skin on, cubed
- 1 tbsp coconut cream

Warm the coconut oil in a deep pot and then soften but not brown the onion, leek and garlic. Add in the spices and cook on a medium heat for a further 2–3 minutes, stirring constantly.

Next add in the chicken thighs, the broth and the quinoa and cook on a medium heat for about 20 minutes. If your chicken thighs are still on the bones, that's great as it will add more flavour to your soup...but you will want to take out the thighs towards the end of cooking and flake the meat from the bones. Return the thigh meat back to the pot and discard the bones. Now add in the remaining ingredients and cook for a further 20 minutes on a low heat.

Top tip... you can use the cream from the top of a can of good quality coconut milk that has gone solid so no need to buy coconut cream specifically.

Tips & Hints

Turmeric is a really good antioxidant and is beneficial for gut health and supporting your immune system.

CAULIFLOWER CHEESE SOUP

This is one of my favourite soups...especially if you need a big bowl of warming, immune boosting deliciousness.

Portion size

Serves 6

Cook time

40 minutes

- 1 tbsp Coconut Oil
- 1 Brown onion, chopped
- 1 Large Head Cauliflower, chopped
- 2 White potatoes, peeled & chopped
- 700 ml stock from bouillon powder
- 400 ml almond milk
- 1 clove garlic, chopped
- 1 can white beans
- Salt & White Pepper to taste

To serve

- 20g Blue Cheese
- 20g Cheddar Cheese
- 40g grated cheese between the 6 bowls.

Heat the oil in a large saucepan. Tip in the onion and cook until soft but not browned, about 5 mins, stirring often. Add the cauliflower, potato, stock, milk, garlic and beans and seasoning. Bring to the boil, then reduce the heat and leave to simmer for about 30 mins until the cauliflower is soft and the potato almost collapsing.

Allow to cool slightly then blitz to a super smooth consistency.

Can be frozen at this stage.

To serve

In a pan add the soup (defrost if frozen) and 20g blue Cheese and 20g cheddar Cheese and bring up to simmer. Serve with 40 g grated cheese between the 6 bowls.

Tips & Hints

Cauliflower is often an underrated cruciferous vegetable – but they are good source of fibre, B-vitamins, antioxidants and phytonutrients, and in particular contain choline which is good for learning and memory.

LENTIL AND CARROT SOUP

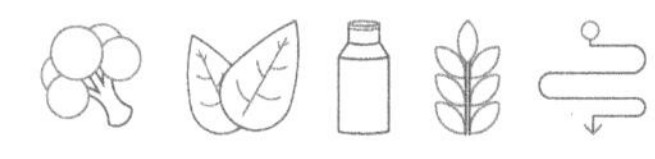

Portion size

Serves 4

Cook time

25–30 minutes

- 1 dstsp coconut oil
- 1 tsp fennel seeds
- 1 garlic clove
- 1 small brown onion
- Salt
- 30g freshly grated ginger
- 700ml vegetable stock from bouillon powder
- 150g red lentils
- 5 large carrots, chopped
- 400g tin chopped tomatoes
- 1 tsp wholegrain mustard
- 1tsp tamarind paste

Warm the oil in a large pan and cook the fennel seeds for a minute then add the garlic and onion and a pinch of salt and freshly grated ginger and cook for 5 minutes until soft.

Add the bouillon stock, lentils, carrots and tomatoes and the remaining mustard, tamarind paste and cook for 20 minutes, stirring occasionally. Remove from the heat and blend half the soup until smooth, then stir back into the remaining soup.

Tips & Hints

The benefit of adding lentils to soups is that it adds protein, iron, folic acid, fibre for digestion and calcium for bone health. Lentils also contain polyphenols which are plant nutrients that help fight against harmful agents in the body.

GAZPACHO SOUP

Portion size

Serves 4

Cook time

No cook

- 700g Firm Tomatoes on the Vine
- 10cm Cucumber (chopped)
- 2 Spring Onions (chopped)
- 2 Cloves Garlic
- 1 Large Red Pepper (chopped)
- 4 tbsp Virgin Rapeseed/Olive Oil
- 1 tbsp Sherry or Red Wine Vinegar
- Salt and Black pepper

To serve

- 2 hard boiled eggs
- ½ green pepper
- 2 slices jamon
- 6 black olives, chopped

Place the tomatoes, cucumber, spring onions, crushed garlic and chopped pepper in a liquidizer, adding a seasoning of salt and pepper, oil and wine vinegar. I like to leave this mix overnight to really allow the flavours to merge.

Blend everything at top speed until the soup is absolutely smooth. (If your liquidizer is very small, combine all the ingredients first, then blend in two or three batches.)

Taste to check the seasoning and pour the soup into a bowl. Stir in a little cold water to thin it slightly – anything from 5–10 fl oz (150–275ml) – then cover the bowl with foil and chill thoroughly for at least one hour.

Serve topped with chopped egg, chopped green pepper, sliced jamon and chopped black olives.

Tips & Hints

Tomatoes are high in carotenoids, lycopene and beta-carotene which are powerful antioxidants that reduce the "rusting" of cells and soak up the potential damaging free radicals.

BROCCOLI, CASHEWS AND DILL SOUP

Portion size

Serves 2

Cook time

10 minutes

- 1 tbsp coconut oil
- 1 clove garlic, chopped
- 2 spring onions, chopped
- 3 sticks celery
- 100g broccoli
- 600 ml vegetable stock from bouillon powder
- 30g cashews, soaked overnight
- 100g fresh spinach
- 1 avocado, chopped
- 2–3 sprigs fresh dill
- Salt

To serve

- 2 dstsp natural yogurt
- 10g raw cashews chopped
- 2–3 sprigs fresh dill

Heat the oil in a large pan and then gently soften (but do not brown as this will give a bitter taste to the soup) the garlic, spring onions and celery – use the pinch of salt to prevent browning. Add the broccoli and bouillon. Cook for 10 minutes.

Add the soaked cashews and spinach and cook for just a few minutes more. Take off the heat. Add the avocado and dill and using a hand blender, blend until very smooth.

Serve topped with a dollop of natural yogurt, some chopped cashew nuts and a few fronds of fresh dill.

Tips & Hints

Avocados in soups makes them thicker and creamier and are a good source of fibre and healthy fats.

CHINESE STYLE CHICKEN AND SWEETCORN SOUP

 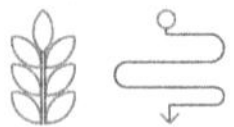

Portion size

Serves 4

Cook time

30 minutes

- 1tbsp coconut oil
- 1 leek, white part only sliced
- 1 sml white onion, chopped
- 1 celery stick, chopped
- 2 garlic cloves, finely chopped
- 4 cups corn kernels – frozen or canned
- 400g Cannellini Beans
- 1 litre chicken stock (or bone broth)
- 500ml water
- 2 dstsp soy sauce – I used tamari to be gluten free
- ¼ sml red chilli – finely chopped
- 2 x 150g skinless chicken breasts, small cubes

To serve

- A dollop of yogurt
- Freshly chopped chilli
- Spring onion.

Tips & Hints

To make vegetarian swap chicken for tofu and chicken stock for vegetable stock.

Heat the oil in a large, heavy-based saucepan (that has a lid) over a medium heat. Cook the leek, onion and celery for 3 mins or until translucent, then add the garlic and cook for 1 min.

Add the corn kernels, white beans, stock and 500ml water. Season to taste with ground black pepper, tamari and chopped chilli. Bring to the boil, then reduce to a simmer and cook for 5 mins. Add the chicken breasts, cover with the lid and cook for 15 mins or until the chicken is cooked through.

Blend about ¾ of the soup until thick and creamy and stir back in the textured portion.

Serve with a dollop of yogurt and some freshly chopped chilli and spring onion.

- French onion tart
- Hot Salmon & Dill Mousse
- Goat's Cheese Mousse with Roasted Apple & Lentil
- Mackerel, Polenta and Roasted Tomato
- Spicy Salmon Barley Bowl

Key to recipes

 – 10 mins or less

 – Vegetarian  – Vegan – Low FODMAP  – Dairy Free – Gluten Free

LIGHT BITES

FRENCH ONION TART

We made this dish for lunch on our French Healthy Holiday and it was always a hit. The recipe was inspired by the wonderful Nigel Slater, whom I love and who is one of my personal kitchen gurus. Working from Nigel's original French Onion Tart recipe I've upped the protein, fat and fibre.

Portion size

Makes 6 Tarts

Cook time

Cook time – 20 mins

Pastry cook time – 10 mins

Bake time – 15-20 mins

- 3 large brown onions, sliced long ways
- ½ tsp dried thyme
- 40g butter
- 375g Puff Pasty
- 150g Silken tofu
- 1 tbsp milk
- ½ tsp Dijon mustard
- 60g pine nuts
- Jar anchovies
- Black olives
- 80g Goat's cheese

Heat oven to 180°C

Peel three large onions, slice them, and let them cook with the dried thyme in a deep pan with the butter until they are sweet, pale amber in colour and soft enough to crush between thumb and finger. This will take a good 20 minutes over a low heat, with a frequent stir.

Take the puff pastry and place it on a lightly floured baking sheet. Score a border, approximately 2cm in from the edges, with a sharp knife, making sure not to cut right through the pastry. Place baking beans in the middle of the pastry and blind bake for 10 minutes.

Blend the tofu with the milk and mustard until soft and silky.

Spread the tofu mix over the pastry then top with the soft onions. Place a good jar of anchovies, maybe more, over the surface, in a lattice effect. Place a small black olive at the centre of each diamond shape. Break up the goat's cheese and sprinkle over the pie, along with the pine nuts. Bake for 15-20 minutes until the pastry is risen and deep gold.

Tips & Hints

Silken tofu it is a softer version of tofu due to the higher water content, made from the soya beans, it contains phytoestrogens that can help balance female hormones – particularly useful during the menopause.

HOT SALMON & DILL MOUSSE

Another recipe from our French Healthy Holiday. I could have called this dish Salmon Soufflé... but then I fear that no one would make it. Soufflés sound difficult, don't they??? To be honest this is a mousse meets soufflé, it has the taste and texture of a mousse but the lightness of a soufflé. Maybe I should call it a Mousffle???? LOL Anyway...whatever you call it, this is a super simple dish to prepare – you can prepare it a day in advance so it makes a great dinner party dish.

Portion size

Serves 4

Cook time

15–20 mins

- 250g Fresh Salmon, Skinned and boned
- 1 large egg separated
- 150ml Crème Fraiche
- 1 egg white
- Knob of butter
- ½ tsp Chopped fresh Dill
- Salt & pepper

Cut the salmon into pieces and place in the bowl of a food processor and give a quick few pulses to begin to break down the salmon. Then add the egg yolk and crème fraiche and process for a couple of minutes until the mixture is smooth but still has little visible flecks of pink salmon. Season with salt and pepper and mix in the fresh dill.

Whisk the egg whites until stiff and then fold gently through the salmon mix using a metal spoon so as not to knock the air from the eggs.

Divide the mixture between four well buttered cocotte dishes and cook in a bain marie in the oven (180°C) for about 15–20 minutes or until the mixture is set.

To serve, unmould each mousse onto a small hot plate and serve with a sauce of your choice and some fresh chopped dill.

Tips & Hints

Salmon is high in omega 3, needed for every cell in your body. Omega 3 is also anti-inflammatory and good for brain health.

GOAT'S CHEESE MOUSSE WITH ROASTED APPLE & LENTIL

Salty savoury cheese, sweet soft apple and firm umami lentils all mixed in with fresh vegetables and salad. This is a wonderful thing. Having a salad with mousse and roasted apple adds texture and heat and colour, making this a very conscious dish.

Portion size

Serves 4

Cook time

15–20 mins

For the salad

- 2 Apples, cored and quartered
- Mixed spice
- 1 can green lentils
- 1 sml bag of baby green salad leaves
- ¼ cucumber
- 4 cherry tomatoes
- 1 sml carrot, cubed
- 1 stick celery, chopped
- 1 tbsp pumpkin seeds
- 2 tbsp walnuts
- Fresh parsley

For the mousse

- 200g goat's cheese
- 8 tbsp milk
- 2 dstsp crème fraiche

To make the mousse

Work together the cheese and milk until it is the texture of whipped cream.

Fold in the crème fraiche, transfer to a piping bag and pop in the fridge to chill for at least an hour before serving. You can also make this up to 24 hours before.

To make the salad

First heat the oven to 170°C, sprinkle the apple slices with a pinch of the mixed spice and roast in the oven for 15–20 minutes until soft and caramelly brown at the edges. Mix the remaining ingredients into a bowl, top with the roasted apple and mousse.

Tips & Hints

Apple skins contain half of the fibre of the apple and contain polyphenol micronutrients from plant-based foods which are particularly good for gut health.

MACKEREL, POLENTA AND ROASTED TOMATO

This is one of my all-time favourite things to eat. Even now as I write this, I can sense my taste buds tingling. It's creamy, it's chewy, it's sweet, it's salty, it's totally moreish.

I haven't eaten polenta for years... I don't know why I ever stopped eating it.

I guess we just fall into habits with the food we eat and can often forget some good stuff.

For those on a gluten-free diet, polenta is a winner, as it's made from ground cornmeal, but it lacks fibre, so often gets overlooked. Here I pair it with delicious local mackerel; as an oily fish, it is a rich source of omega-3 fatty acids.

Portion size

Serves 1

Cook time

20 mins

- 4-5 Cherry tomatoes on the vine
- 10g pine nuts
- 60g polenta
- 100ml milk of your choice
- 5g butter of choice
- 1 tbsp good quality pesto
- 1 tsp rapeseed oil
- 1 large mackerel fillet
- 1 tsp rapeseed oil
- Salt and black pepper

This dish takes only about 10-15 mins to prepare. It is really just cooking the individual elements and then plating up.

Start with the tomatoes, pop them on a baking tray into a hot oven, about 180°C and bake for about 10 mins until soft and just about to pop.

Next place the pine nuts into a dry frying pan and toast until just starting to brown; put to one side.

Now make up the polenta according to the instructions (I made mine with almond milk and added a small knob of butter at the very end).

Heat up your pesto.

When you have all the component parts ready then heat a little rapeseed oil in a pan, season your mackerel and place skin side down in the hot oil. To stop the fish from curling you might need to keep a fish slice on top. Cook for 2-3 minutes and then flip over and continue to cook for about 5 minutes.

To plate up, begin by dolloping your polenta in the centre of the plate, place the fish and tomatoes on top, drizzle with the pesto and scatter on your pine nuts. Eat at once while it's hot...dish delish.

Tips & Hints

To get optimal amounts of omega 3 try to have fish 2 or 3 times a week.

SPICY SALMON BARLEY BOWL

Sometimes what you need is a big bowl of sweet sticky savoury deliciousness. Bowl food may have been seen as a fad thanks to its recent rise to Instagram fame... but haven't we always been eating food from bowls... I'm a huge fan of Conscious Eating and I do find that Bowl Food does tend to support Mindless Eating, scooping away with a spoon, you don't need to even concentrate. So, when you eat this bowl I want you to pay particular attention to how you eat it. Savour every mouthful...and put that spoon down between bites.

Portion size

Serves 2

Cook time

15 mins

- 1 dstsp Soy Sauce
- 1 tsp sweet chilli sauce
- Juice ½ lime
- 2 salmon Fillets
- 1 dstsp rapeseed oil
- 1 cup cooked barley
- 1 avocado, sliced
- ¼ medium cucumber, sliced
- 1 small carrot, grated
- 1 spring onion, sliced
- 2 radishes, sliced
- 30g cashew nuts
- Handful Fresh coriander
- 1 dstsp Toasted sesame seeds

Mix the soy sauce with the sweet chilli sauce and lime juice. Marinate the salmon fillets for at least an hour. Then heat the oil in a frying pan and cook the fillets non-skin side down first. Allow to seal, so do not move the fillets or the pan for at least 5 minutes to allow a crust to form. Flip over and cook for a further 5–10 minutes on the skin side.

Add the other ingredients to make the barley bowl and top with the salmon.

Tips & Hints

When buying salmon make sure you look at the labels ensuring they are fresh, wild and sustainably fished – look for the MSC (Marine Stewardship Council) mark.

- Lemon & Olive Chicken with Butter Bean Mash
- Beetroot & Feta Burger
- Creamy Lentil and Mushroom Curry
- Thai Butternut Squash Curry
- Harissa Turkey with Quinoa Salad
- Courgetti Four Ways
    - Courgetti with Goat's Cheese, Pine Nuts and Cavolo Nero
    - Courgetti with Prawn, Broccoli & Cherry Tomato
    - Courgetti with Turkey Meatball Arrabiata
    - Courgetti with Lentil Bolognese
- Pesto Crusted Cod
- Haddock Risotto
- Lamb Moussaka
- Turkey Fajita Sandwich
- Veggie No Mato Chilli
- Moroccan Lentil Stuffed Aubergine

Key to recipes

 – 10 mins or less

 – Vegetarian  – Vegan 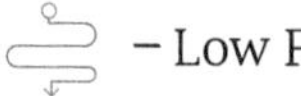 – Low FODMAP  – Dairy Free  – Gluten Free

MAIN MEALS

LEMON & OLIVE CHICKEN WITH BUTTER BEAN MASH

This dish is a retreat staple in the summer months, it's light and very satisfying. Chicken thighs make the best braises; use bone-in thighs for the best flavour. I make my version on the stove top, but this dish is also suitable for oven-braising. To do this make sure that you start the process with an ovenproof dish and transfer to the oven once all the ingredients have been added.

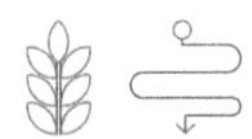

Portion size

Serves 4

Cook time

50 mins

- 4 chicken leg portions, skin off
- 1 tbsp rapeseed oil
- 4 banana shallots, sliced long ways
- 1 stick celery, chopped
- 2 garlic cloves, crushed
- 12 large green olives
- ½ litre chicken bone broth
- 1 sprig fresh thyme
- 1 bay leaf
- 12 large green olives
- 1 preserved lemon, skin only finely sliced
- Salt & freshly ground black pepper
- Handful Flat Parsley, chopped

For the mash

- 2 cans butter beans
- 1 cup milk of choice
- Black pepper

Sprinkle a little salt and pepper on the chicken portions. Warm the oil in a large heavy bottomed pot and then add the chicken (presentation side down first) and allow to gently brown for 3 or 4 minutes. (Do not move the chicken or the meat will stick to the bottom of the pan and then look unattractive when you serve them right side up.) Turn the chicken portions and cook for a further 5 minutes, then remove and set to one side on a plate.

In the pot add a spot more rapeseed oil and add the shallots, celery and garlic, and soften but do not brown. Add the bone broth and herbs and mix well.

Add the chicken portions back to the pot and now add the olives and half the shredded lemon skin. Cook over a medium high heat for about 40 minutes until you can see the chicken is starting to look soft.

At this point check your seasoning and add more salt, pepper or preserved lemon to your personal taste.

Now you can make the mash. Rinse and drain the beans and then add to the pot along with half the milk and seasoning. Bring to a rapid boil, then reduce the heat and cook for 10 minutes until the beans are breaking up. You may need to add the remaining milk as the beans cook so keep an eye on your pan. Now you can mash up the beans with a fork or masher. You can also add a small knob of butter at this point for super creamy mash.

Serve with simple green veggies and sprinkle the dish with the fresh parsley.

Tips & Hints

If you are going to eat meat, I would always recommend you buy free range, organic and local if at all possible.

BEETROOT & FETA BURGER

We love Meat Free Monday, it's a great way to do something positive for your body, your health and the planet…it's the ultimate win/win. It's a chance to eat more plants, increase your menu repertoire. So many of the shop bought veggie burgers are dry and pretty flat tasting. So, if you have tried this kind of veggie burger in the past please don't be put off… this Beetroot Burger will change your mind.

Portion size

6–8 Patties

Cook time

15–20 mins

- 3 cups / 750 ml grated raw beetroots (approx. 4–5 beets)
- 1 Grated carrot
- 1 Small Grated Sweet Potato
- 1 small onion grated
- 2 cloves garlic, minced
- 1 tbsp cold-pressed rapeseed oil
- 1 large egg
- 200g sheep's feta cheese
- 1 handful fresh mint
- Salt and pepper
- 60g Cooked Quinoa
- Coconut oil for frying

Topping suggestions

- Lettuce,
- Avocado
- Tomatoes
- Onions

Peel and grate beetroots, carrot and sweet potato, onion and garlic on a box grater or use a food processor with the grating blades attached. Place the grated vegetables in a large mixing bowl.

Using the mixing blade in the food processor add in half the grated mix and then add the egg and oil and give 2 pulses. Add sheep's cheese, mint, salt and pepper, and stir to combine with quinoa. Set aside for about 30 minutes, so the quinoa can soak up the liquid and the mixture sets (this step is important for the patties to hold together).

Try shaping a patty with your hands. Form 6–8 patties with your hands. Fry them in a frying pan by heating a knob of coconut oil and fry until golden on both sides, then bake in a warm oven for 15 minutes at 180 degrees.

Tips & Hints

These beetroot burgers are a really good alternative to meat burgers. Beetroots contain compounds which are good for heart health.

CREAMY LENTIL AND MUSHROOM CURRY

Creamy, dreamy, heart-warming and healthy...this curry has it all. Richly spiced and yet still mild, with the meaty mushroom and melting lentils this is comfort food that actually does you a whole host of good. Like all good curries this is a one pot wonder that freezes well (although I'd recommend that you do this before you've let the mushrooms cook right down).

Portion size

Serves 4

Cook time

30 mins

- 1 tsp coconut oil
- ¼ tsp cumin seeds
- 1–2 green chillies, chopped
- 1 onion, peeled and chopped
- 2 garlic cloves, peeled and chopped
- 2 plum tomatoes, chopped
- 1 tbsp Tomato Puree
- 1 cup yellow lentils
- 1 tsp garam masala
- ¼ tsp turmeric
- ¼ tsp ginger
- 40g dried mixed mushrooms, reconstituted in hot water
- 200g Mixed Mushrooms, chopped
- Salt and black pepper
- 2 tablespoon natural yogurt
- 1 cup fresh, washed, baby spinach leaves

Heat oil in a medium saucepan. Add the cumin seeds. When they sizzle, add the green chillies if using, and stir for 30 seconds. Then add onion, garlic, and chopped tomato and tomato puree. Stir on medium heat till they are soft, about 5 minutes.

Cook the lentils separately with 3 cups water and add salt. Bring to a boil. Then reduce heat to a simmer. Place a lid on the saucepan and cook till lentils are done, about 15 minutes. Then add the lentils and spices to the tomato mix and stir for 2 more minutes.

Using the back of a wooden spoon, lightly mash the dal, so that the tomatoes and onion pieces are mashed into the lentils. Add the mushrooms and cook for a further 10–15 minutes until the mushrooms are soft.

Add the yogurt and spinach leaves. Stir the spinach leaves into the dal till they wilt, about 1 minute. Add more water to the dal, if needed.

Serve with rice or cauliflower rice.

Tips & Hints

Mushrooms have been known for their medicinal properties, they help keep the immune system working at an optimum level and protect cells and tissues.

THAI BUTTERNUT SQUASH CURRY

This Thai Butternut Squash Curry is packed with aromatic Thai flavours and is indulgent yet healthy. It's quick and easy to make. Keep the skin ON your butternut squash to increase the fibre and nutrition...you'll find that it cooks down beautifully and also prevents the squash from disintegrating if you take your eye off the pan and leave the curry a little longer than intended.

Portion size

Serves 4

Cook time

20 mins

- 2 Small Aubergines or 1 Large Aubergine
- 1 tbsp Coconut oil
- 2 Medium Onions, chopped
- 1 stick celery, chopped
- 2 Cloves Garlic, crushed
- 1 tbsp Red Curry Paste
- 1 Stick Lemongrass
- 1 Kafir Lime Leaf (optional)
- 1 Medium Butternut Squash& chopped
- Salt and pepper to taste
- A dash of fish sauce (optional)
- 1 Can Chickpeas
- 1 Can Coconut Milk
- 1 tbsp Tomato Paste
- 1 Large Red Pepper, chopped large
- 1 Small Head Broccoli, chopped into small florets (add at the end)
- 1 large handful Fresh Spinach
- 1 Large Handful Fresh Coriander

Heat a large heavy pot over medium-high heat. Add the coconut oil, soften the onion then add the curry paste and stir for about 1 minute, or until fragrant. Meanwhile remove the hard-outer layer from the lemongrass stick and then bash what remains with the back of your knife to release the flavour and add to the pot.

Add the squash and stir to coat with the curry paste. Stir in the chickpeas. Add the coconut milk, tomato paste and ½ a cup of water and bring to a simmer.Reduce the heat to medium-low, cover, and simmer gently for about 10 minutes, or until the squash just begins to soften.

Stir in the red pepper, broccoli and gently simmer, uncovered, stirring occasionally, for about 10 minutes, or until the squash is tender but not falling apart and the sauce has reduced slightly. Season to taste with freshly ground pepper and fish sauce.

Remove the lemongrass and lime leaf and stir through the spinach leaves. Divide the curry among four soup bowls, top with chopped coriander, and serve.

Tips & Hints

1. One pot cooking is a lot less fuss and by batch cooking you can freeze portions for healthy ready meals at a later date.
2. As an alternative to serving with rice, think about serving with cauliflower rice.

HARISSA TURKEY WITH QUINOA SALAD

I don't like Hot Spicy food, but I do Love Tasty Spicy food...one of things that I love about spices is being able to layer up the spice to what works for me. On retreat we always keep things pretty mild – it's better to know where to start from and if it's not spicy enough you can always add a little more...you can't really unspice a dish if you've been too heavy handed. This Harissa Turkey is a great way to start your journey into experimenting with spice.

Portion size

Serves 4

Cook time

1 hour

- 400g turkey breast, cut into strips
- 1 tbsp harissa paste
- 1 tbsp rapeseed oil
- 1 onion, sliced
- 2 garlic cloves, crushed
- 1 tsp ground cinnamon
- 1 tsp ground cumin
- 400 ml stock of your choice
- 4 apricots
- 1 x 400g tin chopped tomatoes
- 2 stick celery, sliced
- 1 sml carrot, sliced
- ½ courgette, sliced
- ½ aubergine, cubed
- 1 large handful fresh baby spinach
- Salt and freshly ground black pepper
- 2 tbsp freshly chopped mint
- 2 tbsp freshly chopped parsley

Coat the turkey strips in the harissa paste and leave to one side as you prepare the vegetables.

Heat the vegetable oil in the base of a tagine dish, or heavy-based casserole dish. Fry the turkey for 2-3 minutes. Remove from the dish using a slotted spoon and set aside.

Fry the onion for five minutes, or until soft. Stir in the garlic and spices.

Add the meat back to the dish, along with the stock, apricots and tomatoes, then add in the other veg. Season with salt and freshly ground black pepper. Bring to the boil, cover with the lid and simmer for one hour

Serve with cooked quinoa and garnish with fresh herbs.

Tips & Hints

Harissa (which is a North African hot chilli pepper paste) is made from various peppers which are good for heart health and help to reduce inflammation.

COURGETTI FOUR WAYS

You'd have needed to be under a rock these last few years to have missed the Veggie Spaghetti revolution. Veggie spaghetti is great way to boost your nutritional intake, lighten your meal and is a godsend if you are grain-free. Once you have your spiraliser you will be hooked. Now the key to great Courgetti is to bake rather than steam or boil... you need no moisture added to your courgetti. After spiralising make your courgetti into nests and bake in a warm oven for about 5-10 minutes. You want them to just wilt a little but still keep a delicious bite... your sauce or topping of choice will then have something to stick to and you don't end up with a puddle on the bottom of your plate.

Courgetti or Courgette Ribbons

If you haven't already tried raw courgette spaghetti that is all about to change. This is such a great alternative to pasta. I tried many, many, many times to perfect recipes I read on the internet but somehow always seemed to end up with mush. This way is fool proof, I use it all the time on retreat when I can be catering for up to 10 people...not a mushy noodle in sight!!

The key is fresh firm courgettes, the older they are the higher the water content and the less good the noodle.

Serves 4

4 large very firm courgettes

Either spiralise your courgettes or use a peeler to create full length ribbons.

Then place the ribbon in a colander over a bowl and leave for up to an hour to dry out a little.

About ten minutes before you need them form your ribbons into nests on a lined baking tray and pop into a warm oven, about 140°C is good. Allow to gently warm up.

Using a fish slice place a nest on each plate and top with your sauce or dressing of choice.

Tips & Hints

Courgettes are actually a fruit and are high in antioxidants – the highest levels are found in the skin and are good for eyes, skin and heart.

COURGETTI FOUR WAYS

Portion size

Serves 2

Cook time

5 mins

Cavolo Nero, Goat's Cheese & Walnut Courgetti

- 100g Cavolo Nero (Italian kale), chopped
- 1 tbsp Rapeseed oil
- 1 Clove Garlic, Minced
- 40g Walnuts
- Pinch salt
- 60g Soft Goat's Cheese

Warm your oil in a shallow pan over a medium heat, add your chopped cavolo nero, the garlic and a scant pinch of salt. Allow the cavolo nero to just wilt and then take off the heat straight away. Mix the walnuts through the kale and then immediately top your courgetti. Crumble over your goat's cheese and eat straight away.

Portion size

Serves 2

Cook time

5 mins

Prawn, Broccoli & Cherry Tomato Courgetti

- 100g broccoli, cut into small florets
- 150g Frozen Jumbo King Prawns, fully defrosted
- 1 tbsp rapeseed oil
- 100g cherry tomatoes, halved
- Lemon juice
- Salt and pepper
- 25g Pine Nuts, lightly toasted
- Pinch dried chilli flakes

Place 2 tbsp of water into a shallow pan and when it has come to a gentle simmer add your broccoli and cook for a couple of minutes, then add the defrosted prawns and watch as your prawns turn from grey to pink. As the water evaporates add the oil and cherry tomatoes and a squeeze of fresh lemon juice and pinch of chilli flakes.

As soon as your prawns are cooked (they will be fully pink and hot all the way through) add a pinch of salt and black pepper.

Use to top your courgetti along with the toasted pine nuts and an extra squeeze of lemon.

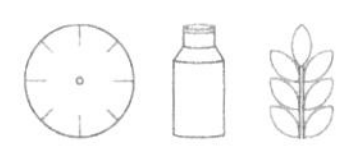

Portion size

Serves 4

Cook time

10 mins

Turkey Meatballs Arrabiata Courgetti

- ½ Onion
- 2 Garlic Cloves
- 500 g Ground Turkey
- 50g Quinoa flakes
- 1 Egg
- 1 tsp mixed herbs
- ½ Onion, finely chopped
- 1 Carrot, finely chopped
- 1 Green Pepper, finely chopped
- 1 Can Chopped Tomatoes
- 1 Tbsp Tomato Concentrate
- 200ml Chicken Stock
- Dried Mixed Herbs
- Dried chilli flakes
- Salt & Pepper

First to make your meatballs: Cut the onion in half and finely chop one half along with one clove of garlic. In a frying pan heat ½ tbsp oil and gently fry the onion and garlic to soften. Then in a large mixing bowl combine the turkey, the onion mix, the quinoa flakes and egg. Mix together to thoroughly combine. Then use a soup spoon to measure out 16 meatballs from your mixture.

To make the sauce: Sauté the vegetables with the other half of the onion in a tsp oil until soft but not brown, add the tomatoes and tomato puree, stock and herbs and simmer until reduced.Top your courgetti with three meatballs and a generous dollop of arrabiata sauce.

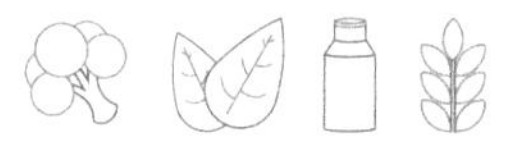

Portion size

Serves 4

Cook time

45 mins

Lentil Bolognese Courgetti

- 1 tsp rapeseed oil
- ½ onion, finely chopped
- 1 sml carrot, chopped
- 1 stick celery, chopped
- 1 clove garlic, chopped
- 160g green lentils
- 1 can chopped tomatoes
- 2 tsp tomato puree
- 1 bay leaf
- ½ tsp mixed herbs
- 200ml vegetable stock
- 1 handful chopped spinach
- Salt & black pepper
- 2 small firm courgettes for courgetti

Heat the oil in a large saucepan and add the onions, carrots, celery and garlic add a pinch of salt. Cook gently for 15 mins until everything is softened. Stir in the lentils, chopped tomatoes, tomato purée, herbs and stock. Bring to a gentle simmer, then cook for 30 mins until the lentils are tender. Add the spinach, give a good stir through and then take off the heat. While the bolognese is cooking, spiralize the courgettes and make into two large nests on a baking sheet. 10 minutes before you are ready to serve, heat the courgette nests in a warm oven.

Bolognese can be frozen or kept in the fridge for a few days. Just keep second courgette to use fresh again.

PESTO CRUSTED COD

Another Retreat staple, I like to serve this soft but still firm fresh fish, topped with a salty, herby nutty pesto crust accompanied by the rich tomato loveliness of Ratatouille and simple cooked green beans when they are in season. This is a very good thing. You can keep the pesto in a jar in the fridge for a couple of weeks and use in other dishes for a quick supper dish.

Portion size

Serves 1

Cook time

20 mins

- 125g cod fillet

For the pesto

- ½ sml head broccoli
- Rapeseed oil
- ½ clove garlic
- Handful fresh Parsley
- 25g cashew nuts
- 10g mixed seeds
- Rapeseed oil
- Salt & Black Pepper

Another Retreat staple, I like to serve this soft but still firm fresh fish, topped with a salty, herby nutty pesto crust accompanied by the rich tomato loveliness of Ratatouille and simple cooked green beans when they are in season.

This is a very good thing. You can keep the pesto in a jar in the fridge for a couple of weeks and use in other dishes for a quick supper dish.

Tips & Hints

Cooking with herbs like basil in this recipe not only add flavour but have proven health benefits. Basil is one of the oldest herbs known to man, it aids digestion, can help fight infection and may even help lower cholesterol levels.

HADDOCK RISOTTO

Sometimes you just want a sloppy bowl of warming comforting food. But that doesn't need to mean stodge! Don't be scared to make risotto; yes, you need to be on hand to do a bit of stirring, but it's easy. This sustainable smoked haddock is a thrifty fish to use and gives a wonderful flavour.

Portion size

Serves 2

Cook time

20 mins

- 450ml milk
- 300g smoked haddock
- 2 bay leaves 2
- 6 black peppercorns
- 450ml fish or vegetable stock
- 250g wholegrain basmati rice
- 40g butter
- 2 handfuls spinach leaves
- 30g frozen peas
- 2–3 chopped chives

Pour the milk into a saucepan large enough to just cover the fish. Place the fish in the milk, add the bay leaves and peppercorns, then bring to the boil. As soon as the milk shows signs of foaming, lower the heat and simmer for 2–3 minutes or until the fish is just tender. Turn off the heat and leave the milk to infuse with the fish and aromatics.

Gently heat the fish or vegetable stock in a saucepan. Place the rice in a pot and then add the stock a ladle at a time, allowing each one to be soaked up by the rice before adding the next.

Once all the stock has gone, change to the milk, strained of its peppercorns and bay leaves. By the time almost all the liquid is absorbed the grains should be tender and plump yet with a slight bite to them. Fold in a thin slice of butter and season carefully. The total cooking time will be about 20 minutes, maybe a few minutes longer.

Wash and chop the spinach leaves into small pieces then stir them into the rice, along with the peas. Break the fish into large, juicy flakes and add them to the rice, folding them in, but keeping the flakes as whole as possible. Top with a few chopped chives.

Tips & Hints

Haddock contains B vitamins, magnesium, selenium and omega 3. The tip for this recipe is that in allowing the milk to infuse with the fish and aromatics will make a good fish risotto.

LAMB MOUSSAKA

Traditional Moussaka tastes so good due to the fried aubergine slices and the heavy creamy sauce that holds the dish together. Which is fine for an occasional treat, but what about a midweek supper dish? Here we have baked the aubergine and lightened up the sauce by using yogurt ... You won't miss the old version – this is bound to become a new family favourite.

Portion size

Serves 6

Cook time

Stove top –15 mins

Oven – 20 mins

- 2 large aubergines (approx. 700g total weight), sliced into 5mm thick rounds
- 300g potatoes, skin on, sliced into 5mm thick rounds
- 1 tbsp Rapeseed oil
- 1 onion, diced
- 1 celery stick, diced
- 3 garlic cloves, crushed
- 400g lamb mince
- 2 x 400g cans chopped tomatoes
- 2 tbsp tomato purée
- 2 tsp dried oregano, plus an extra pinch
- ½ tsp ground cinnamon
- 3 tbsp chopped fresh mint leaves
- Salt and pepper
- 200g Greek yogurt
- 1 egg, beaten
- 50g feta, crumbled

Heat the oven to 180°C

Spread the aubergine slices over the baking sheets, then cook in the oven for 15 mins. Remove and set aside but leave the oven on.

Meanwhile, bring a medium pan of water to the boil, then add the potato slices and cook for 5 mins. Drain in a colander, then rinse under cold water, drain again and set aside.

Heat the oil in a large heavy based pan. Cook the onion, celery and garlic with a pinch of salt, stirring constantly, for 5 mins or until softened. Add the lamb mince and cook, stirring with a wooden spoon to break it up, for 5 mins. Add the chopped tomatoes, tomato purée, oregano, cinnamon and mint and stir to combine. Season to taste with ground black pepper and cook on a low heat for 8–10 mins.

While the meat mixture is cooking, combine the yogurt and egg in a small bowl, then set aside.

Put a third of the meat mixture into the base of a large ovenproof dish. Top with a layer of potato slices, then a layer of aubergine. Repeat the layers until all the ingredients are used up, finishing with a layer of aubergine on top.

Pour the yogurt and egg mixture over the moussaka to evenly cover. Crumble over the feta and sprinkle with a pinch of oregano, then cook in the oven for 20 mins or until golden and bubbling at the edge.

Serve with a simple salad.

Tips & Hints

To make a vegetarian option you could swap the lamb for green lentils.

TURKEY FAJITA SANDWICH

This dish is inspired by Julie Brealy's favourite foods. Julie loves Mexican style food, loves a sandwich, loves eating with her hands... This Turkey Fajita Flatbread ticks all the boxes.

Portion size

Serves 1

Cook time

40 mins

- 1 tsp rapeseed oil
- 50g Turkey Breast, cut into strips
- 1 tsp smoked paprika
- ½ tsp mild chilli powder
- Pinch dried oregano
- ¼ Red Onion, long slices
- ¼ Red Pepper, long slices
- 1-inch carrot, long slices
- ¼ ripe Avocado
- 1 tsp Natural Yogurt
- Juice of half a lime
- 1 tsp fresh coriander leaves, finely chopped
- Salt and black pepper
- 1 Wholegrain seeded Pitta Bread
- Handful Rocket leaves
- Sprouted Seeds

Heat the oil in a large frying pan and add the turkey strips and cook over a medium heat, turning regularly for about 6–7 minutes.

Next add the spices and dried herbs, the onion, peppers and carrot, add a pinch of salt and cook on a medium heat for about 5 minutes until the veg is softening and just starting to brown.

Mash up your avocado along with the yogurt, a pinch of black pepper and a squeeze of lime juice and the fresh coriander.

Squeeze the remaining fresh lime juice over the turkey and veg mix.

Now you are ready to construct your sandwich. Warm your pitta bread or taco and then fill with rocket, add the turkey and veggies and top with the avocado dressing and a generous pinch of sprouted seeds.

Tips & Hints

You could substitute bread for iceberg lettuce leaves to make an equally tasty but lighter sandwich option.

NO MATO VEGGIE CHILLI

This is a dish that we have made for a lovely retreat returner who hates Tomatoes... well to be honest they hate her too. So when she joins us on retreat, we bring out the No Mato Sauce. Yes, there is a bit of preparation and the precooking of the sauce, but one of the best bits about this sauce is that it freezes beautifully, so make a big batch and freeze in portions so that you can then defrost and use in a variety of No Mato ways.

Portion size

Serves 6

Cook time

40 mins

No Mato Veggie Chilli

- 2 tablespoons rapeseed oil
- 1 medium red onion, chopped
- 1 large green pepper, chopped
- 2 medium carrots, chopped
- 1 medium sweet potato, chopped
- 2 ribs celery, chopped
- 2 handful fresh spinach leaves, chopped
- 1 tsp hot paprika
- 1 tsp ground cumin
- ½ tsp ground coriander
- ½ tsp chilli flakes
- 1 can kidney beans
- 1 can black beans
- Handful fresh coriander

No Mato Sauce

- 1 tbsp Rapeseed oil
- 1 large Onion, chopped
- 1 stick Celery, chopped
- 1 garlic clove, crushed
- 1 Parsnip, chopped
- 2 Carrots, chopped
- 1 large cooked Beetroot, chopped
- 2 cups bouillon stock
- 1 teaspoon dried Oregano
- Handful fresh Basil, chopped
- Salt & Pepper to taste

To Make the No Mato Veggie Chilli

Heat the oil in a large non-stick pan. Add all the vegetables and cook, stirring frequently for 8–10 minutes, until starting to soften. Stir in the spices, season, then cook for 30 seconds. Add the kidney and black beans and no mato sauce. Partially cover the pan and simmer, stirring occasionally, for 30 minutes until the vegetables are tender.

Serve with rice and garnish with coriander.

To Make the No Mato Sauce

Heat the oil in a heavy based pan and cook the onion, celery and garlic until soft but not browned. Add the remaining ingredients, except the basil and cook for about 15 minutes until the vegetables are very soft. Add the fresh basil and blitz until smooth.

You can now use this sauce for a variety of No Mato dishes. Bolognese, arrabiata, Chilli... anywhere you would normally use a tomato-based sauce.

Tips & Hints

1. Using fresh herbs and spices add flavours that have a variety of health benefits.
2. Making a versatile sauce is a way of getting lots of vegetables into a sauce without knowing it.

MOROCCAN LENTIL STUFFED AUBERGINE

I'm going to be truthful with you and share that Aubergine is my devil food…except in two versions. As a tapas when it's roasted and served with local honey or here when the delicious depth of Moroccan spiced lentils takes this humble vegetable to a new level.

Portion size

Serves 2

Cook time

15–20 mins

- 2 Small Aubergines or 1 Large Aubergine
- Rapeseed oil
- 1 Onion, diced
- 2 cloves of garlic, minced
- ½ tsp ground cumin
- ½ tsp cinnamon
- ¼ tsp ground cardamom (or use 1 cardamom pod – just remember to remove it)
- Pinch of Salt & Black Pepper
- 1 clove
- Fresh or crushed chilli or chilli powder to taste
- 2 large Tomatoes chopped or 1 Tin of Chopped Tomatoes drained
- 1 small courgette, diced
- ½ can Green Lentils, rinsed
- 1 handful baby spinach
- 1 tsp toasted pine nuts
- Fresh Coriander or Parsley Leaves

Assemble the ingredients for the stuffed aubergine recipe before you start cooking

Preheat the oven to 180°C

Cut the Aubergine in half length ways but not right through. Make criss-cross cuts into the aubergine flesh, taking care not to pierce the skin and pop on a baking tray and cook in the oven for about 20–25 minutes.

Meanwhile fry the onion gently in a saucepan with rapeseed oil for about 5 or 6 minutes until just beginning to turn translucent and golden.

Add finely chopped garlic and the spices and cook for a further 3–4 minutes. Add the tomato, courgette and lentils to the saucepan and cook for 10–15 minutes.

Remove the partially cooked aubergine from the oven, use a spoon to scrape out the filling and chop up into small pieces, then add this chopped aubergine to your pan of veggies, add the baby spinach leaves and mix through. Now fill your aubergine cases with the mixture from the saucepan.

Pour a tablespoonful of water over the top and in the dish – spread pine nuts over the top and drizzle with rapeseed oil.

Bake the stuffed aubergine in the oven for about 15 minutes until lightly browned on top. Serve topped with the fresh coriander or parsley.

Tips & Hints

The purple colour of aubergines signifies a high antioxidant content of plant goodness for health.

- Smoothies
  - Greenacolada
  - Glowgetter
  - Very Berry Blast
  - Pretty P Smoothie
- Chocolate Fudge
- Fake Wheaten Bread
- All In Banana Bread
- Retreat Crackers

Key to recipes

 – 10 mins or less

 – Vegetarian  – Vegan 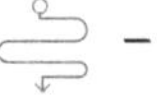 – Low FODMAP  – Dairy Free – Gluten Free

SNACKS & SMOOTHIES

SMOOTHIES

Smoothies are made by blending the ingredients. This means putting whole pieces of fruit and vegetables in the blender, so none of the fibre gets lost.

Portion size

All make one Snack Size Smoothie

Cook time

No cook

Tips & Hints

Smoothies are a good way of getting a variety of foods with a balance of protein, fat and fibre, while remaining delicious.

Greenacolada

"If you like Greenacoladas, and getting caught in the rain"...I'm showing my age here but I can never make these smoothies without singing this song...mostly to myself but I've been known to croon it out to retreaters too.

- 1 ring fresh pineapple
- 1 handful baby spinach
- 1 dstsp natural yogurt
- 50ml coconut water
- 75ml coconut milk
- 1 tsp ground flaxseed

Place all ingredients in a NutriBullet and blend until smooth.

GlowGetter

I've called this smoothie so many names over the years on retreat as the recipe has been tweaked over the years. The glow refers to the avocado which is amazing for your skin and the older I get the more I'm concerned about eating for good skin.

- ¼ ripe avocado
- ¼ ripe mango
- 1 handful fresh spinach
- 1 inch cucumber
- 75 ml coconut water
- 1 tsp hulled hempseeds

Place all ingredients in a NutriBullet and blend until smooth.

Very Berry Blast

Three lovely words for you...Healthy Slush Puppy. This is a green juice that really isn't green...yet is still packed with goodness.

- 100g frozen mixed berries
- ½ grapefruit, peeled and segmented
- 1 inch cucumber
- 1 handful spinach
- 75 ml coconut water
- 1 tsp ground flaxseed

Place all ingredients in a NutriBullet and blend until smooth.

Pretty P Smoothie

A sweet greens smoothie with an unusual sweet ingredient... Frozen peas.

- 75g frozen petite pois
- Large handful fresh spinach
- 25g hulled hemp seed/cashew nut butter
- 1 large sprig mint
- 200ml coconut water
- 1 tsp green powder

Put all ingredients into your NutriBullet and blitz until very smooth. Enjoy immediately.

Sweet P Smoothie

A sweet greens smoothie with an unusual sweet ingredient... Frozen peas.

- 75g frozen peas
- Large handful baby leaf spinach
- 25g hemp seed
- 40g fresh pineapple
- 1 cup coconut water

Put all ingredients into your NutriBullet and blitz until very smooth. Enjoy immediately.

CHOCOLATE FUDGE

Being dairy free now, I thought that fudge would be a treat of the past. I have made other no-cook fudge with nut butter and seeds and they are nice enough...but fudge isn't meant to be nice enough. Fudge is meant to be indulgent, delicious. This vegan fudge is amazing!! Shop bought fudge ingredients can consist of lots of refined sugars. It can also include ingredients such glucose syrup, butter, golden syrup, sweetened condensed milk (yet more sugar) and sometimes even chemical flavourings. These are rich and creamy fudge cubes; while they do have less sugar than regular fudge and a hit of protein in the addition of flaxseed, they are not going to win an award for the healthiest of treats so one cube is a portion.

Portion size

Makes 10/12 squares of fudge

Cook time

7 mins

- 150g dark chocolate
- 50g vegan butter
- 120ml coconut milk (full fat)
- 200g coconut sugar
- 25g ground flaxseed
- Pinch sea salt

Line small loaf tin with parchment paper

Break up the chocolate and mix into the vegan butter.

Add the milk and sugar to a saucepan and bring to a rapid boil, stirring continuously. Set a timer for 7 minutes and continue to stir on a rolling boil.

Take off the boil and add in the butter chocolate mix and stir vigorously and quickly while incorporating the flaxseed and salt.

Transfer to the lined loaf tin.

Place in fridge to cool and set for at least 1 hour.

Once fully set and hard to touch, remove from tin and cut into small bite size squares.

Can be kept in freezer or fridge for up to one month.

Tips & Hints

You may get more nutritional benefit from eating ground flaxseed rather than whole linseeds as the outer hull is so tough that it will pass through you undigested and you miss out on the benefits of the healthy fats.

FAKE WHEATEN BREAD

This bread reminds me of the loaves my grandmother used to bake when I was growing up. Crumbly, chewy, moist and seriously moreish.

Portion size

One Loaf

Cook time

45 mins

Make a starter

- 150ml warm water
- 1 tsp honey
- 70g buckwheat flour
- 1 tsp quick action yeast
- 2 tbsp psyllium husks

For the dough

- 25g ground flaxseed
- 35g whole linseed
- 40g hulled hemp seed
- 50g ground almonds
- 80g chia seeds
- 150ml hot water
- 3 tbsp rapeseed oil
- 1 tsp honey
- Pinch salt
- 125g Oat flour
- 100g buckwheat flour Line small loaf tin with parchment paper

To make the starter

Mix the water and honey. Mix the flour, yeast and husks. Gradually mix in the dry to the wet, stirring constantly. Cover with a tea towel and leave to rise at room temperature for 30–60 mins.

To make the dough.

Mix the seeds and ground almonds together. Mix the water, oil, honey and salt. Then combine the two flours with the water mix and stir well. Now combine all the ingredients together, the starter, the mixed seeds and the wet mix. I use the batter mix blade on the mixer. Turn out the mixture onto a lightly floured work surface. Knead the bread a couple of times to ensure an even mix of all the seeds. Form into a large round ball. Plop onto a lightly greased baking tray. Place a small bowl of water on the floor of the oven and then place the baking tray in the middle of the oven. Bake for about 45 minutes until golden brown. Remove to a wire tray and allow to cool completely before cutting.

Tips & Hints

Do you need to go gluten free? In short NO. Not everyone should follow a Gluten Free Diet. Gluten appears to affect people on a differing scale. Where some have coeliac disease, or other autoimmune conditions and gluten needs to be avoided completely. At the other end of the scale there are people who have no sensitivities to gluten and can tolerate it fine. In between there are people that may be sensitive to varying amounts of gluten and find that being gluten free their health and gut feels better for it.

ALL IN BANANA BREAD

There are so many versions of banana bread. I like mine as it's a consistent bake for us non-bakers. A slice for a snack or two slices as part of a healthy breakfast.

Portion size

One Loaf

Cook time

1 hour

- 3 cups of frozen banana (defrosted)

Wet ingredients:

- 60g melted butter
- 1 tsp vanilla
- 2 large eggs
- 2 tbsp milk

Dry ingredients

- 75g sugar – I used coconut sugar
- 150g flour – I used GF
- 1 tsp baking powder
- 1 pinch salt
- Pinch cinnamon
- 50g oats
- 25g ground flaxseed
- 75g chopped pecans
- 50g hulled hemp seed
- 80g chopped dates
- 2 tbsp milk

Mix the wet ingredients together with the bananas – then add in the dry. Add a little milk if needed to make a thick batter consistency that you can pour into your parchment lined loaf tin.

Bake in the oven for about 1 hour. Use a skewer to test if done. Leave to cool in the tin for 30 mins and then turn out and allow to cool completely before cutting.

Tips & Hints

You can keep bananas in your freezer – take ripe bananas, peel and slice and freeze, they should be good for a few months.

RETREAT CRACKERS

These grain-free seeded crackers are a hit on retreats when we serve them alongside a big bowl of comforting soup.

I've been making these crackers on retreats for years now and they are always popular. I used to make these using my dehydrators and so didn't share the recipe until I had perfected the oven method.

Portion size

One loaf

Cook time

1 h 10 min

- ½ cup sunflower seeds
- ½ cup pumpkin seeds
- 1 cup walnuts
- ½ cup chia seeds
- 2 cloves garlic, crushed
- 2 teaspoons freshly chopped herbs
- 1 tbsp vegan yeast, optional
- Generous pinch of salt and black pepper
- 1 cup warm water.

Preheat your oven to 140°C

Soak your sunflower, pumpkin and walnuts in warm water for at least an hour. Drain your seeds and nuts but keep the soaking liquid.

Place all the ingredients into your food processor and blitz until well combined. If your mix is too dry, then slowly add in some of the soaking liquid.

Spread your mixture onto a flat baking tray lined with baking parchment. Using a metal spoon or your damp hands, press down until flat and level. Cut the crackers now before you place the tray in the oven.

Bake for about 30 minutes, remove the tray from the oven and flip the cracker sheet over and remove the baking parchment. Put back into the oven and cook for a further 30–40 until completely dry.

Tips & Hints

Seeds are a great source of vegetable protein and are high in omega 3 oils; cooking makes them more digestible and the nutrients more available.

- Fig and Hazelnut Bark
- Lemon Mousse
- Coconut Bars
- Jaffa Cake Biscuits
- Baked Fruit with ginger crumb
- Strawberry Ice Cream
  & Banana Pecan Ice Cream
- Double Chocolate Pistachio Cupcakes

Key to recipes

 – 10 mins or less

 – Vegetarian  – Vegan 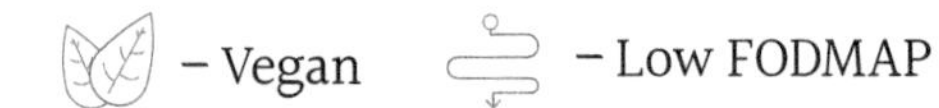 – Low FODMAP

SWEET TREATS

FIG AND HAZELNUT BARK

When did we start to call chocolate bark?? I don't know the answer to that one, but I do know that this is delicious. I started to make this after giving up dairy – while I like a little of the dark stuff you do need something to take the edge off the bitterness. This is where the fig and hazelnut come in, they soften the bitterness while adding in something interesting for your taste buds to latch onto.

Portion size

Serves 1

Cook time

NO COOK

- 300g 70% Dark Chocolate
- 1 dstsp Cocoa Butter
- 100g Hazelnuts, chopped
- 40g Dried Figs, chopped fine
- Pinch Sea Salt.

Line a cookie sheet with foil or waxed paper. In a medium microwavable bowl, microwave chocolate and cocoa butter on high for 1 minute, stirring once halfway through microwaving, until melted. If necessary, continue to microwave on high in 15 second increments, stirring until smooth.

Stir the hazelnuts, chopped figs and salt into the bowl of chocolate. Spoon the mixture onto the cookie sheet; spread evenly to about ¼-inch thickness. Refrigerate until firm, about 1 hour. Break into pieces. Keep in fridge.

Tips & Hints

We all need to indulge in a sweet treat from time to time. The benefits of dark chocolate which contain antioxidants and polyphenols, particularly flavonoids, have been shown to be beneficial for heart health and improve brain function – just remember to enjoy in moderation.

LEMON MOUSSE

Light, sharp, sweet and small... everything you want after an indulgent meal or at the end of a diner party. We served these little pots on our French Healthy Holiday.

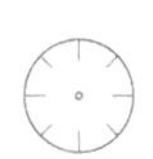

Portion size

Makes 6

Cook time

NO COOK

- ½ pack silken tofu
- 2 tbsp coconut cream
- 2 tbsp runny honey
- Juice and zest of a large unwaxed lemon
- ½ tsp agar
- 2 egg whites

Whisk the tofu and the coconut cream until smooth. Add the honey, lemon juice and zest and agar and mix again until well combined and super smooth. Check for lemoniness and add more lemon zest if you like your mouse to be a little sharper.

Whisk the egg whites until stiff and then gently fold into the lemon mix using a metal spoon so as not to deflate the air. Spoon into your glasses and chill in the fridge for at least an hour before serving.

Tips & Hints

Lemons are a good source of vitamin C and can help aid digestion.

COCONUT BARS

Sweet milky coconut and dark bitter chocolate, what an amazing combination. This is probably one the very first things I can ever remember making, way back in primary school, except my coconut bars then were made with condensed milk and cooking chocolate... sugar overload. These little bars are the grown-up version of my primary school efforts.

Portion size

6–8 Bars

Cook time

NO COOK

- 200g unsweetened desiccated coconut
- 1 tbsp maple syrup or honey
- 2 tbsp virgin coconut oil, melted
- 1 tbsp soft coconut cream (from the top of a full fat coconut milk is good)
- ½ tsp pure vanilla extract
- 200g 70% + Dark Chocolate
- Scant pinch of sea salt

Place the coconut, the maple syrup, the coconut oil and cream and the vanilla into a food processor and blitz until well combined. Use a tablespoon to portion out your bars and then using your hands mould into bars. Pop into the freezer for at least an hour before you are ready to coat.

When the bars are hard and you are able to handle them easily, remove from the freezer and place the bars onto a wire rack if you have one, if not a plate will do...but we are about to get messy. Melt the chocolate, either in a bowl above a pan of water or in the microwave in 30 second blasts. Mix the salt into the melted chocolate.

Now you can either pour the warm chocolate over the bars on the tray or dip each bar into the melted chocolate. Put the bars back in the freezer on the rack or plate if you can accommodate it. We don't want the bars touching or the chocolate will stick together. Once they have hardened up you can remove the rack/plate and store your bars in a sealed box for about 6 weeks. Just remove from the freezer at least 10 mins before you want to eat them ...or you may lose a tooth LOL!

Tips & Hints

Coconuts are high in manganese, which helps to metabolise the macro nutrients – protein, fats and carbohydrates and it is also essential for bone health.

JAFFA CAKE BISCUITS

Funnily enough I wouldn't thank you for a "real" Jaffa cake biscuit. That orange jelly and dry sponge... but chocolate and orange are a beautiful thing together.

Portion size

12 Biscuits

Cook time

8–10 mins

Dry Ingredients

- 100g rice flour
- 50 g buckwheat flour
- 50g ground almonds
- 2 heaped tbsp cocoa powder
- Pinch sea salt

Wet ingredients

- Juice of 1 large orange
- 4 tbsp honey
- 3 tbsp rapeseed oil
- Zest of two large oranges

Preheat the oven to 190°C

Line a large baking tray with parchment paper.

Combine the dry ingredients in a large bowl. In a jug mix the wet ingredients including the orange zest. Pour the wet ingredients into the dry and mix well to ensure that it is thoroughly mixed into a firm dough. Bring together into a large ball and then roll to about 2cm thick between two piece of parchment paper. Using a cookie cutter, cut into 12 biscuits.

Towards the end you may find you need to roll back together the remnants to form a dough ball and once again roll out between the parchment sheets. Bake in the oven for 8–10 minutes. Leave to cool completely before eating. Store in an airtight container for up to 2 weeks.

Tips & Hints

What is buckwheat flour? Buckwheat is not actually a grain (not a cereal or grass) but it is a fruit which is related to wild rhubarb. To make the flour the husk is removed and the inner pod is ground down to make flour.

BAKED FRUIT WITH GINGER CRUMB

Fruit Crumble is good in every season as there is almost always a seasonal fruit that you can top with a crumble. In early spring you have rhubarb, then into berries through summer, into orchard fruits in autumn and then I love citrus in winter.

Portion size

3-6 Portions

Cook time

20 min

- 3 Peaches/ 3 apricots
- 1 tbsp Oats
- 1 tbsp Buckwheat Flour
- 1 tsp sugar (we use coconut, but use what you have)
- ½ tsp cinnamon
- ½ tsp ground ginger
- 1tbps coconut oil

Remove the stones from the peaches, then use a teaspoon to remove a little more of the flesh so as to make the hole a little bigger. Place on an ovenproof dish.

To make the crumble topping, mix all the remaining ingredients together then pour over the peaches.

When you are ready to eat place into a hot oven for about 10-15 minutes until the peaches soften and the crumble goes toasty brown.

Tips & Hints

There are natural oils in ginger – gingerol has been used in traditional medicine for its anti-inflammatory and antioxidant effects.

STRAWBERRY ICE CREAM & BANANA PECAN ICE CREAM

I love ice cream; before I went dairy-free it was always my go-to pudding. These two ice-creams make a delicious dairy-free alternative and the best bit is that they take only a couple of minutes to make and you don't even need an ice cream maker just a decent powerful blender. I love the NutriBullet for this.

Portion size

Serves 2

Cook time

No cook

Strawberry Ice-cream

- 10 large frozen strawberries
- ½ frozen banana
- 1 tbsp full fat yogurt

Place all the ingredients into your blender or NutriBullet and whiz until very smooth

Banana Pecan Ice Cream

- 1 frozen banana
- 1 heaped tsp nut butter
- 1 dstsp chopped pecans
- Splash of milk to get the blender started

Place all the ingredients into your blender or NutriBullet and whiz until very smooth

Tips & Hints

You can make many alternatives by using different berries.

DOUBLE CHOCOLATE PISTACHIO CUPCAKES

Who doesn't love a muffin and a cuppa in the mid-afternoon??? Now you know that I'm going to recommend that you have a small protein-based snack most afternoons to help keep your blood sugar balanced, but there are days when you just fancy a little something. So why not have the best of both worlds, a muffin that is sweet and delicious and packs some protein power too.

Portion size

Makes 12 cupcakes

Cook time

20 min

Dry ingredients

- 150g almond flour
- 85g cocoa powder
- 150g gluten free plain flour
- 1½ tsp baking powder
- ½ tsp bicarbonate of soda
- 1 generous pinch sea salt
- 1 tbsp pistachios, chopped

Wet ingredients

- 3 eggs
- 4 tbsp rapeseed oil
- 4 tbsp maple syrup

Topping

- 100g dark chocolate
- 2 tbsp pistachios, chopped

Preheat oven to 180°C

In a large mixing bowl mix together all the dry ingredients. In another bowl whisk together the eggs, oil and maple syrup. Mix the wet ingredients into the dry and fold in to make a batter.

Pour the batter into 12 cupcake cases in a cupcake tin. Bake for 20 minutes or until a toothpick come out clean from the centre. Allow to cool completely before you top.

To top. Melt the chocolate and using a dessert spoon pour a little of the melted chocolate into the centre of each cupcake and then top with the chopped nuts.

If you want to freeze them do this before you top the cupcakes. Allow to defrost thoroughly before you then add the topping.

Tips & Hints

A fact about pistachios is that a serving of 49 nuts has the same amount of protein as an egg! But that is not a serving... remember your portion sizes LOL

RECIPE INDEX

BREAKFAST

Key to recipes

 – Vegetarian

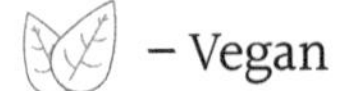 – Vegan

 – Low FODMAP

 – Dairy Free

 – Gluten Free

 – 10 min. or less

SALADS

SOUPS

LIGHT BITES

Key to recipes

 – Vegetarian

 – Vegan

 – Low FODMAP

 – Dairy Free

 – Gluten Free

 – 10 min. or less

MAIN MEALS

SNACKS & SMOOTHIES

Key to recipes

 – Vegetarian

 – Vegan

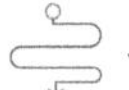 – Low FODMAP

 – Dairy Free

 – Gluten Free

 – 10 min. or less

SWEET TREATS

ACKNOWLEDGMENTS

I swore after we finished Conscious Cooking book 1 that I would never write another cookery book. Luckily for me, Ms Brealy had more faith in me than I did myself and here you have the evidence of her faith: Conscious Cooking 2. This sums up our partnership perfectly, we are a team; while it may be my name on the book, without her support and encouragement I would never have sat back down at the laptop. So, a huge Thank You, Julie.

I also must thank all our Body Retreaters who over these past few years have asked me, with that little knowing smile, when the next book would come out. Alongside Ms Brealy you have kept me accountable and I thank you so much for that. I also want to thank you for all your feedback on the meals you have enjoyed and maybe even endured on retreat. While most of my experimental cooking happens at home, there have been occasions when I've used retreat as a testing ground LOL!

Thank you to Sally Mortimore for being my right hand through the process, making sense of my notes and scribbles and helping me to get the book across the line.

Thank you to Yolande de Veres for another fabulous fun photoshoot.

Thank you to Jane Alexander for your integrity in your quest for wellbeing, you are an inspiration to so many women and I am very proud to know you.

First published in Great Britain in 2021

Editing, design and typesetting by UK Book Publishing

www.ukbookpublishing.com

ISBN: 978-0-9955313-1-4